THE MARVELLOUS KINGDOM

*

PIERRE LABAT

Translated from the French by
MAURICE MICHAEL

ODHAMS PRESS LIMITED
LONG ACRE, LONDON

First published in England 1956

This book has been formerly
published in French by
Alsatia, 17 rue Cassette, Paris

Made and printed in Great Britain by
Wyman & Sons Limited, London, Reading & Fakenham

To the Memory of

ALAIN JUSTOME

and of all those who, like him,
died because of a too great love
for the
Marvellous Kingdom

ILLUSTRATIONS

7

PREFACE

IT was July and *Calypso* was tied up in the arsenal of Toulon getting ready to undertake some difficult submarine archæological excavation off the Grand Congloué islet outside Marseilles.

We were intending to recover the cargo of a Greek merchantman that had sunk in 22 fathoms some time during the third century B.C., and even to raise the hull itself. It was a considerable undertaking and would be possible only if we had the assistance of numerous disinterested persons.

Pierre Labat came aboard to offer me his services and those of several of his fellow Scouts. I had met him only once before and now scrutinized him in an attempt to weigh him up. Who was this Troop Leader who each year took thirty or so boys to the sea and initiated them into the art of free-diving? What was his object in coming to us? What could he get out of devoting himself to the least profitable of all ventures?

As though replying to these questions, which I did not dare put to him, Labat with a faint smile handed me the manuscript of this book. A glance or two at it and I had no further doubts; the future was to confirm and enhance that good impression.

Labat was one of those who have the finest mission of all, that of inspiring youth and getting it to conquer the splendours of Nature, of revealing to it the profound joy of striving and even of gratuitous risk, for happiness, or simply balance of mind, are not to be won in the mere struggle for a decent life. Those who died on the slopes of Everest and Annapurna, those like Fargues and Servanti

9

who have died in deep-diving, are themselves the expression of a civilization in which man requires much more than just his daily bread.

Pierre Labat and Raymond Kientzy spent their New Year's Eve with us on a rocky islet pounded by the sea. At midnight they dived into the cold, black water and brought up from the wreck an amphora that is symbolic of our faith.

J. Y. COUSTEAU

Lieutenant-Commander.

PUBLISHER'S NOTE

We deeply regret to record that in August, 1955, Pierre Labat dived for the last time into the Marvellous Kingdom.

THE jagged cliff plunged steeply down to the sea with a promise of depth. Ahead of us, holding his heavy watertight camera in both hands, the heavy apparatus already strapped to his back, George slowly made his way down from rock to rock. The three of us, Alan, Claud and myself similarly harnessed, followed carrying the rest of our equipment: deflated rubber dinghy, masks, frogmen's-feet, weighted belts and daggers.

Philip had remained behind in our camp on the other side of the rise, by a little wood of stunted pines, from where we could still hear the muffled panting of the three-stage compressor busy charging our reserve cylinders. We undressed in silence on a narrow rocky platform by the water's edge. George opened the taps, put his lips to each in turn of the mouthpieces or chromium-plated leads of the masks. At each inhalation the automatic reducing-valve released the exact quantity of air necessary. All was well.

The rest of us were already putting on frogmen's-feet.

"Francis, you've forgotten your dagger. Claud, inflate the dinghy."

Slowly the black rubber dilated and took shape.

Then while Alan, who was not yet seventeen, knelt with one knee on the ground, we loaded him with the three long steel cylinders, in their light frame of steel plate, that was fixed to his back with rucksack straps. He stood up, and staggered, like a youthful squire trying to carry his knight's armour; but in a few minutes the kindly water would have relieved him of all the weight.

"Embark!"

All five of us piled into the little dinghy, wearing frog-men's feet and with breathing apparatus strapped on. The rubber sausage bent and became misshapen beneath our excessive weight, and as we moved the dinghy writhed like a flabby animal. Slowly we floated out towards the open. The water was sparkling for as far as we could see; the air was filled with a strong smell of hot, wet rubber, and a feeling of drowsiness came over us.

"Francis, check your marks."

"A bit more to starboard . . . that's it . . . stop!"

The mooring rope ran out.

"Put on your masks. Open the cylinders."

Claud and George jammed the mouthpieces of their Cousteaus against teeth and gums. Alan and I were using Commeinhes GC 47. It was all so easy. Almost as easy as in a fairy tale; just a few turns of the wheel on the left-hand cylinder. The water-tight masks exactly fitted our young faces. The rubber extended to the extreme point of chins, covered our cheeks and up to our temples by the corner of the eyes, and the inflatable cushion round the rim made them perfectly watertight. An arrangement of straps and buckles with a crowfoot at the back of the head held them firmly in place, like a second face superimposed on the first, the face of our submarine existence. At each inhalation the reducing valve resisted slightly before, with a whistle, it released the minimum column of air. That caused a slight feeling of distress and we had to inhale strongly to make the needle-valve open and admit the vital air to our masks. Breathing was a conscious act and being alive became a praiseworthy thing. When we inhaled, the air came in on the left-hand side of the mask and expunged the vapour misting the glass before escaping after exhalation by the delicate valve on the right-hand side. Thus the good fresh air no longer came direct to our lungs and our windpipes were extended by lengths of rubber tube. Alternately opening and shutting, an artificial glottis sent us puffs of life. When our lungs inflated, the valves gaped, air circulated in the pipes, the pressure fell slightly in the cylinders and the little pointers on the faces of the gauges moved back imperceptibly. When we exhaled a spring moved and a fragile valve opened to let the air escape.

A delicate system of tubes and valves had become geared to our own organs of flesh and blood, tubes that were flooded in time with our bronchial valves that palpitated in time with our diaphragms. Whole live parts of us were now made of metal and rubber.

"Into the water. Dive."

We went into the soft welcoming water, one from each side simultaneously, frog-footed feet first, and hands still clutching the rubber sausage. Then we let go and were under in a fizz of foam and bubbles, and the next moment all was silence and limpidity, a symphony in blue. All four of us assembled a few inches beneath the bottom of the rubber dinghy treading water with slight movements of our frogmen's feet, while we held our last council of war. Trickles of bubbles escaped from the right-hand temples of our Commeinhes masks in time with our breathing, or from behind the backs of the necks of the two who had Cousteau reducing-valves fixed to the tops of the cylinders.

"Thumb-up"—"thumb-up"—"thumb-up." All was well.

We were privileged ones with access to the Marvellous Kingdom where Man is not allowed to dwell, going to take advantage of the fleeting minutes allowed us there. Strapped to our bodies was the magical apparatus that protected us. George stretched out his arm, pointed his index finger towards the depths, then his body tilted and he dived, thrusting into the haze with great scissor movements of his legs.

Go! Trailing four plumes of silver behind us we swept after him towards the bottom of the sea.

A little out of line, I watched the other three ahead of me: Alan, Claud and George in front. I imagined them swallowing fiercely behind their masks or mouthpieces in order to equalize the pressure on their ear drums. In the luminous water their slow-motions were invested with a wonderful harmony. Their irregular movements gave an impression of haste and grotesque confusion. Then the uneasiness passed, whatever its cause, and they lay elongated, aware only of the glory of gliding without weight down an immaterial slope.

With the bottom of the boat shaded out, there was nothing but blue to see, through the window of the mask, a deep blue; the blue of medieval stained glass; fixed and unchanging; blue on the right, blue on the left; blue below, and when you lifted your head even the surface had already disappeared behind a haze of blue.

Twenty-eight on the wrist bathometer; the bottom could not be far. All of a sudden there it was with its sand and bushes of sea-fans like rushes powdered with white. It was the Sahara in winter-time, little submarine islets, black rocks, a hazy yet visible world, and a palpable one in place of the unchanging sea-green water pressed throughout the descent against the glass of our masks.

George straightened out and swam on, skimming the sea-floor, the great camera held in front of him. A wall of silvery fish, streaked with gold, burst and closed again behind us. At the limit of vision on the left three high-finned mullets swam mistrustfully away; then more silvery fish and round-eyed lampreys, calm and stupid. They pivoted all at the same time, and the formation opened like a series of shutters giving a glimpse of a grassy slope, then it turned back on its original course and again there was the compact formation of sparkling sides.

George knew his way about. We had to follow a valley where the anemones had just come out like magic palm trees, each a brownish trunk, with the protective stem that they secreted fixing them to the rock, while their branchiæ waved at the top like a bunch of purple leaves. Some took cover abruptly as we approached, the fragile crest being suddenly withdrawn inside the tube, the end of which then shut up, lips closing in over their secret. In a moment or two, when we have gone, perhaps the delicate petals will emerge again and unfold in a slowly ascending spiral.

All around us were white or yellow sea-fans, motionless and extended. Each was a cloudy colony of animalculæ on the watch, and rather like an asymmetrical, petrified fern. If one of the cells in the community captured any fragments in suspension it would soon let all the rest of the colony benefit, from the fine extremities stretched by the thrust of the water towards the distant surface, to the dumpy foot, bell-mouthed like a blunderbuss and firmly fixed to a cavity in the rock.

The sea-green haze hanging over the gully made it like a tunnel. George was ahead of us, a dark shadow poised in the gap that was powdered blue with bubbles.

One hundred and twelve feet and we were among huge sea-fans like screens, their outline indeterminate, seeming blue or green. In the filtered light of the depths they looked blue or green, yet take them up to the daylight, or turn an artificial light on them, and you would see that they were really a purplish red.

Alan glided head first into a horizontal fissure, then

withdrew brandishing an irregular branch; red coral. Apparently the fissure was full of it, but without a water-tight lamp we could not conjure up the magic of the hidden brilliant colours. George was growing impatient and gestured to order us on.

One hundred and thirty feet. When you put a finger into it, the sand on the bottom felt heavy and fluid, like mercury. It was here that some days before I had met Long-Arms, the octopus. She was crossing from one side to the other in a series of supple propulsions, tentacles folded back behind her and undulating like tresses, and there was about her a sort of equivocal grace as though she were a bad fairy disguised for a few moments as a princess.

Slowly a silvery glow became apparent. George caught sight of it, turned on to the diagonal and began filming the big *denti* that, heavy and mistrustful, was following the length of the valley. After one stealthy glance at the strange fish that we were, it did not deign to look at us, but the tactile streamers on its squat back must have been painfully aware of the thrusts of our frog-feet and of the silvery bubbling of our rhythmically escaping breath.

Strange it thought us; then, suddenly making up its mind, it put on speed and was gone. Perhaps, before we arrived, it had surprised Long-Arms in the open, in the middle of the valley. Look out, if that had been the case! Long-Arms must have released her ink, then voluntarily sacrificed one or two tentacles to save the rest, before plunging into the jungle of rocks where the seaweed would at once have closed behind her.

The valley began to widen, then petered out in a barren desert about which were scattered occasional poor oases of seaweed.

A dark, blurred mass appeared straight ahead of us and

there at last was the object of our pilgrimage, the wreck. The stern, one propeller buried up to the boss, an iron side with port-holes like caves. A thick-lipped *merou* retreated towards the stem. Guardian spirit of the forbidden sanctuary, what did it think of our visit? A swarm of black sea-bream seethed above the gutted hull.

She must have been a proud ship when she was launched fifteen years before, no doubt with flowers and speeches, and with someone to cut the ribbon and break a bottle of champagne. Then came the getting under way. The paintwork would be immaculate, the brass shining, and the captain feeling proud as he paced the spardeck that now lay rotted and cracked beneath a sea-green haze.

Five years old she had been when she set sail for the last time, bound for the Piraeus with a mysterious cargo in her holds.

The breaches made by the two torpedoes were to port, on the other side, but it was on this, the starboard side, that was the neat geometrical cut made by the Italian divers with their blow-pipe.

Under the stern you could still make out the letters MAKAS AR in oxidized copper. The second S was missing. We had removed it the year before.

We knew that behind the curtain of haze other hulls must be lying, and farther on others again, like marks laid throughout the centuries to blaze the trail of the great sea routes. One by one they had come, turning round and round as they sank; some were metal hulls holed by mine, torpedo or gun, or shattered by the sea; others wooden hulls now rotted and dismasted like lighters, covered in sand or draped in shrouds of the concretions of the centuries.

These ships' bones piled beneath the dangerous passes, there submarine cemeteries to which, like elephants, the

17

ships had come to die, to us their attraction was irresistible. We already knew several of them: there was *Tozeur* gone aground on Rattoneau after being driven out to sea; at the foot of Planier Lighthouse there was *Dalton* which split herself open on the rocks on Christmas night 1903 with her crew dead drunk; near Maire Island was *Liban* which had collided with *L'Insulaire*; north of Cape Bear was *Saumur*, like *Makassar* split open by torpedoes, and now swarming with crayfish.

There she was, *Makassar*, torpedoed in 1941.

George skimmed along level with the side, shot up over the bulwarks that were coated with velvet slime and covered with clusters of excrescences, then, arms and legs spread wide, dropped gently on to the quarter-deck like a tired octopus. First, a glance at his water-tight chronometer, for at that depth no dive may exceed twenty minutes, as otherwise the stages of decompression soon become prohibitive.

The group reassembled, like a ballet of ghosts, a weird confabulation of masked, anonymous beings, swaying in slow motion beneath 130 feet of water. There was Claud's streaming hair, its redness lost beneath the spectral light, the peeling paint of George's cylinders, and at the edge of his mask his scar, still the same but darkened by the ghostly light. I was entranced by the exactitude of all these familiar little details and the miracle of finding them in this world of dreams and unpredictable possibilities.

All at once George handed me his huge watertight camera, then he glided away, skimming the bridge, bent double, and dipped into a hatchway. For a moment his two frogmen's-feet were the only things visible, then they too slid into the shadowy hole. A puff of silver came trickling up and was scattered: George must have been threading his way towards the bows through the gloom of a fore-and-aft gangway. Personally I have never had the courage to venture inside a wreck, and I admired George for doing so. Perhaps one day I will. I too readily imagine myself getting wedged between two angle-irons, or putting my hand in the dark on foul and filthy things that give limply beneath it.

Five yards farther on, level with the davits, a fine diamond froth began to seep through and rise from the fissured deck. George was progressing surely towards the bows, twining in and out among those petrified ruins. Perhaps he had already got farther than that sprinkling of air would seem to indicate, for its rise was slow and it must have taken bubbles exhaled beneath the deck some seconds to filter through the cracked plates. At last, from the next hatchway at the limit of vision, came a free gush of bubbles, then a masked head emerged, then two big cylinders of metallic blue. George, restored like Lazarus from the tomb, returned towards us in a long and effortless glide. Somewhere inside George must have caught his mask on something making it shift and leak, for there was water three-quarters of the way up the thick glass. Using both hands, George carefully readjusted his mask, then he slowly turned over on his back and while continuing to breathe in through the mouthpiece, exhaled each time through his nose thus expelling the water under the rubber rim. Then a few bubbles appeared at the level of his temples. That was it, the mask was almost empty. A half-roll and George was on his back again. Then he took the camera from me and signed to me to swim across the bridge so as to pass within the field of his view-finder so that my fleeting figure might later be proof of the presence there of man. It was all the mere stuff of dreams, of course. At least I was part of George's dream, as he of mine.

Slowly I passed in front of his lens, threading my way through the stub derricks and the windlass that was covered with seaweed which waved in the current of my passage. The funnel was inclined to port; I levelled out at the deck plates and then rose vertically up to the bridge, where was the ship's bell. Its rope had gone, but something prompted me to strike the two double strokes which mark ten o'clock, apparently the hour at which MAKASSAR went down. It was a muffled sound, dull and weird, that came from the bell of that phantom ship. The Italian diver in his copper mask had not had time to haul himself so far, or he had been content to perform the burglary he had been told to make and had not bothered about other things. That bell would be for us. Before we left the island we would dismantle it, and so take with us the soul of the ship, instead of its cargo that we had been denied.

There was the gaping opening and I slipped into it obliquely so as not to let the cylinders catch, and there indistinct in the semi-darkness were the wheel and the compass.

Ten o'clock of an April morning. The helmsman caresses the spokes of the wheel, head slightly tilted back, eyes fixed on the distance and dropping at moments to observe the faint oscillations of the compass. Heading south.

Outside the wind is sovereign (I actually read the log at the owner's and that recorded that at the moment of being torpedoed there was a breeze "settled in the north, moderate to fresh gale, squalls "). No doubt the men of the watch are scanning the green water, huddled in their pea-jackets, caps pulled down over their eyes, trouser-legs taut against their shins and flapping out behind like flags. Then come the explosions, columns of water that wash the deck, shouts, orders, cascades of thudding feet on the ladders.

"Ahead ", "astern", "ahead", bells ring for the last time, hands let go of the twin grips of the Chadburn now covered with algae.

"SOS. SOS. Freighter *Makassar*. Have just been torpedoed . . ."

Holding my mask so that it should not shift and leak I edged into the wireless operator's cabin, my pale hand setting off an explosion of small black fish which were suddenly all round me.

"SOS. Freighter *Makassar*. SOS . . ."

There was no one there now, but then it was 1941 when *Makassar* went down. I came out again on the port side of the bridge. The shoal of black fish had reformed above the funnel like a belated plume of smoke.

Thump, thump, I heard. But the engines were no longer revolving. It was just that in turning I had knocked one of my cylinders against the steel-plate. Then silence, dead silence.

"SOS. *Makassar*. SOS."

The submarine, having scored a hit, would already have turned and be making off like a big, blind shark. Unless it had waited for its victim to die, watching through its periscope while it lay like a monstrous toy just below the cellophane of the surface.

"Abandon ship!"

After that no sound comes from the speaking-tubes now stopped up with shell-fish. The copper-sheathed wheel moves softly, becomes still for ever. The only thing still alive is the old compass that turns with a slow regular movement as the ship swings round: 230—240—250. It has always shown how she is heading—and it did so yet beneath its sheath of accretions.

Hurried steps, all the hatchways are opened on the ravaged deck. There are no boats left on the davits, only the hawsers hanging like gallows' ropes. The siren on the left of the funnel moans, three hurried sounds, then the long bellow of the mortally wounded creature. The last vibration of the bell dies away. The masts tilt, a steady glide, the stern-post submerges, then the slow descent like a falling leaf in an eruption of bubbles.

It was all finished and for ever. The men had left. The wheel with its velvet covering of algae was wedged at "hard to port" and the monstrous petals of the screw had finished mashing the green water; there was no need of it on that last, silent, motionless voyage.

Yet I could still hear in imagination the moan of the siren giving its signal of distress, a whistling sound that made me feel unreasonably disturbed. Only the spell could not last for ever; its effectiveness oozed away with the bubbles escaping and making their way back towards the light. The gauge at my belt showed only 22 lb. Already the rubber of the mask was being pressed in against my face. A little feverishly my hand groped for the chromium-plated wheel of the last bottle and turned it. The whistling sound stopped abruptly. Fresh air flooded the mask, wiping away my distress along with the mist on the glass. Hurrah! man and his plans are infallible!

Ten feet above the deck George was hovering vertically, counteracting his imperceptible weight with slight movements of his feet. Suddenly his movements became more rapid, larger. The frogmen's-feet bent gracefully under the pressure of the water, and George rose straight up, like a god, his plume of bubbles suddenly reversed and flowing down. We, in our turn, followed, performing the same miraculous ascent.

The compressed air withdrawing from our middle-ears caused a queer crackling in our ear-drums. Beyond the haze above us sparkles already showed where the surface was. Like arrows we hastened with great strokes of our flippers towards the light. We still had to wait for three minutes at ten feet beneath the dinghy, the dark shadow of which we could see outlined above us and to the left. That wait was to let our blood, which was charged with nitrogen by the pressure, have the time to purify itself smoothly and without releasing bubbles, instead of discharging them all at once, as when a bottle of lemonade is opened. The time was marked on the gauge, the time to return to our exile among people, admitting that the Marvellous Kingdom did not belong to us entirely. Even so, when that evening round the fire of our bivouac we closed our eyes in sleep, the things we would see in our dreams would have no connexion with the arid monotonous earth. We realized that now, though of them, we could not be altogether like other people.

2

IT was the second time we had camped on the island near the wreck, a sterile naked island lashed by the seas and the wind and with nothing to remind you of man. The sailors of the *Galatée* who in 1862 fetched water and buried one of their number there, had to get back to their ship at once because the wind was making the two long ribbons of their caps beat frenziedly. It is a desolate rock burned by the sun and encrusted with salt where it is above water, but from six feet below the surface, where it is sheltered from the furious squalls, and down to the sandy bottom, the sheer sides are covered with a luxuriant cloak of motionless fauna, and in the sea itself, either alone or in clusters, in shoals, in flocks, streamlined bodies live their lives. Thus, insects and lizards apart, the only animal life we had seen for the last four months was what we found below the surface of the sea. We ourselves were no longer very sure that we belonged to the earth, for we spent the most of our time either a hundred feet below the surface with steel cylinders on our backs, or else drowsily on the surface having just thrust the little breathing tube between teeth and gums, but always wearing our rubber frogmen's-feet, and really to be accounted part of the submarine fauna.

It was only in the evening when we had to slip into our rough, warm, sailor's clothes that we regained consciousness of being human, yet each morning when we came out of the tent to strip at once and stand shivering in the freshness of dawn we underwent our metamorphosis and were restored to the sea.

Before continuing this journal of our dives and the history of our submarine adventure since it first began six years ago, let me say that this book is in no way an attempt at justification. All that I shall have to say will, I expect, produce rather the opposite effect. It is, after all, established that those who condemn us have appearances on their side: we have been madly rash, at the beginning out of ignorance and later much less innocently. That is especially true of last year during our first camp on the island, and again last spring when that accident happened to Claud. George has nearly killed us all, and myself on several occasions. And I have done the same in different circumstances.

When our eyes happen to meet there lights up in them the same little flame as we remember the deadly risks we have run, George and I. We are each other's victims and abettors and that links us together more firmly than the ordinary ties of friendship, however great. Our accusers have a fine time recalling us to a sense of our duties and responsibilities, taxing us with failure to realize what we are doing or with "homicidal mania", and applying to us all, and especially to George, concise, definitive and condemnatory epithets.

The truth, of course, is more complex. There are several Georges, as no doubt there are several of the rest of us too. Life does not have the distinct outlines of a drawing, and it is only in novels that individuals are whole and coherent. There is the prudent, meticulous George who examines the equipment before each dive, and there is the heedless George who under water risks his life for pleasure; there is the vain George strutting in front of journalists, and the simple, candid George admitting the justice of the dressing-down he has had from his father. There is the kind, thoughtful George who makes you put on his jersey when you are shivering with cold after a long dive, and there is the George of two hours ago who, when I was trying to persuade him not to make us dive in rather a nasty sea, turned and said "Good heavens, are you afraid?" with a little laugh that was more of an insult than any slap on the face.

All these Georges merge to make up this tall, fair-haired adolescent who will kill us, or perhaps we him, but for whom we at any rate would have no hesitation in letting ourselves be killed.

And then ours is a different world, and we are aware of observing different rules. Our accusers can have no idea of how quickly such words as "prudence", "responsibility", etc., lose their values under the enchantment that is renewed each time we visit our Marvellous Kingdom. Even when we have returned to the surface the spell is not broken, rather is it stronger, enhanced by our nostalgia. We have drunk the love philtre, the magic has worked, the "damage" is done and we would not have it otherwise for anything in the world.

And I am sure that were our wise accusers to cross the frontiers of our domain, they too would forget everything in order to follow that fish that was disappearing in the haze of the depths, or, intoxicated with the silence and the solitude, they would try to cull a moving flower from some steep side.

* * *

It all began six years ago. The first time I saw him was at the seaside. He was by himself, jumping from rock to rock among the pools. He was wearing a sailor suit with long trousers, large square collar down his back and the ribbon of his cap had printed on it in letters of gold *Titanic*. It was a bit short at the wrists and ankles and it would have made any other boy of thirteen look ridiculous. To me, however, it gave him an air of mystery which attracted me at the same time as it rather intimidated me. Every now and again the wind off the sea would lift his big collar and thrust it fluttering like a flag against the hollow back of his fair head. I could not help thinking then of a young cadet survivor of some ancient wreck or of a little northern prince exiled from his kingdom to some sea-swept island.

The boy was coming towards me, so I was now better able to see his big forehead, narrow temples and eager eyes. From time to time he stooped and, using his knife, prised something from the rock. I saw him take a little brown sea-urchin between finger and thumb and raise it level with his face. As he drew near, I could easily see the articulated spines of the shell waving slowly in all directions.

The boy put the sea-urchin down, squeezing it carefully into a cavity in the rock and then opened it along the equatorial line. For a long time he remained absorbed contemplating its anatomy, then, suddenly making up his mind, he ate it whole, as he would an oyster, with an expression of such pleasure that I was surprised. Then he carefully threw the two halves of the shell back into the sea.

"You can never tell with the brown ones", he said. "It's best to see if the spikes have left a space round the lantern of Aristotle. You can always eat the red ones, at least here, because I suppose there are other kinds. You must always throw the shells back into the sea, because then they disintegrate quickly and cannot hurt those who want to dive."

I was nonplussed, but also fascinated. I wanted to ask him what a lantern of Aristotle was, but I didn't dare and so contented myself by taking up the phrase about diving.

"Do many people come and dive here?"

"No, nobody. . . . There are some pink ones farther down, twenty or thirty feet from the bottom, with five slices like melons; I have seen them when the water was low and very clear. There ought too to be star-fish and anemones, yellow and mauve ones, and perhaps also white sea-fans lower still."

He paused for an instant, then added, honestly:

"But I haven't seen those."

Then for a while neither of us spoke. In the end it was I who, blushing, resumed the conversation.

"Do you live in the town?"

"Yes, since last week. And you?"

"I too."

"My name's George."

"I'm Francis."

"Let's go on."

He removed his cap and with the utmost calm put a dozen dripping sea-urchins in it.

We went back by the deserted harbour. Behind the wharfs, with their leprous walls tattooed with political slogans, rose the masts and funnels of big ships that had no swell to rock them. But a swing-gate barred our way: No Entrance. With the utmost unconcern George climbed over it, merely asking me to hold his cap with the precious sea-urchins while he did so. Then I passed it to him through the bars.

"Come on!"

By myself I should never have dared, but even then I found him impossible to resist. As we crept across the narrow railway tracks and among the pyramids of sacks George explained in his frank little voice:

"It's closed here on Sunday, and the watchmen don't matter."

We reached the sea again at the end of an avenue of cases and barrels, but it was not the same sea of a short while before with its red rocks. Trapped by jetties and break-waters, it was a captive, dirty and scarcely pulsated against the side of a big black ship. Polluted with fuel oil, it had lost its mysterious depth and its bluey-green, and had become a dreary mirror for dark hulls with gory patches of red lead.

"You see that big one there, all white, with a raked funnel? That's *Kairouan*. I was in a fishing boat when she stopped to meet the pilot-boat. The pilot-boat goes out to them when they are signalled off the 'Maire' by the semaphore."

"She's a good looker", I hazarded.

"Pooh! She can scarcely do 15 knots. She sails the day after tomorrow."

The very words went to my head and I could so easily see the departure: the goodbyes, the long siren notes, the tugs floundering as they tried to shift the heavy hull, then the ship's shiver as, once through the harbour channel, the swell of the open sea took her on the beam, and the navigation lights being lit before she plunged into her first night.

George went on:

"All sorts of boats have berthed here, tied up to these dead bodies. Then they have sailed again. Some to the scrap heap, to rust and rot in some inner dock, or else to be handed over to the breakers-up with their blow-pipes; others rest at the bottom of the sea, for always. . ."

A siren moaned in the distance. The phrase, "others rest at the bottom of the sea, for always", stuck in my mind and gave me an eerie thrill. New pictures passed

29

before my mind's eye: wrecks covered in mud, split open, crushed beneath motionless water, scrap-iron in and out of which swim multicoloured fish, a macabre sight that you find difficult to believe is true, yet was as real as that harbour, those cranes and all the other familiar things that are real, yet safe from the indiscreet gaze of man.

"At the bottom of the sea", George repeated. "Come home to me. I want to show you something."

His right hand stopped its nervous fingering at the knot of the black silk scarf on his chest. With an impulsive gesture he tipped all the sea-urchins out of his cap and threw them into the water. Then he put on his cap, the *Titanic* ribbon almost over his eyes, and thrust his fists into his trouser's pockets with a gesture of resolution. Then he no longer looked like a schoolboy.

"Oh, I'll get there", he said. "Sooner or later I'll manage it."

I have never regretted what happened that day, the last Sunday of the summer holidays when I was twelve. We scarcely spoke while we walked from the harbour to his home, and I did not dare ask my new friend what it was he wanted to show me.

In the hall of the house where George's parents lived we met a young woman.

"So here you are", she said to George.

George introduced me: "This is Francis . . ." and went straight on:

"Do you know, Mother, I collected some sea-urchins and anemones . . . no not the anemones. Not yet. They were too deep, later. And I've thrown the sea-urchins back."

George's mother smiled at us. She seemed to know what George was going to show me, for she said to him, putting her hand on his head:

"And try not to flood more than the bathroom this time."

We went up to George's room and there I saw the first material sign of the Adventure, our Adventure. Triumphantly George waved in front of my nose a Czech army rubber gas-mask, its filter snout stoppered with a bung which was itself pierced by what looked like a lead drainage syphon strangely twisted back.

*   *   *

George is now a tall, fair-haired, muscular young man asleep in the tent beside me. I can hear his regular breathing accompanied by the noise of the sea breaking rhythmically on the rocks of this desert island. Our adventure is at its height, this adventure that began six years ago on that Sunday I shall never forget.

George dragged me mysteriously into the bathroom, bolted the door, then turned on the taps of the basin, both taps to fill it more quickly, until it was brimming. Then, still in the same solemn silence, he put on the mask which had big goggles, fastened the straps at the back of his head, tried the mask to see if it was tight by breathing out while keeping the end of the breathing pipe closed with his hand. Yes, it was air-tight, for the mask went flat.

Then he plunged his head deep into the basin. For the next two or three minutes he stayed like that, motionless, blowing like a grampus, his ears crimson and half submerged. Then when he was upright again, he said in a voice in which there was already a note of triumph:

"I can breathe and I can see."

Then he made me try the apparatus. I put on the mask and thrust my head in. It was true; I could see the bottom of the basin, the chromium-plated plug and the little chain with absolute clearness, as if there had been no water there. It was then that for the first time I smelt that smell of damp rubber which was to become for us the very perfume of adventure. I did not pay any notice to it then, for I still thought it just a toy of George's, quite clever, but of no real consequence. The importance of his "invention" quite escaped me.

I had ample time to realize it later. George is impatient with those who are slow on the up-take. That day, however, I was both his guest and his new friend. Besides, he was so happy that I don't think he could have been angry. Anyway what he most wanted was an audience to whom he could expound the merits of his apparatus, and he at once launched out into a learned explanation all about the fluid of the eye, equal and different indices of refraction, the formation of images on or behind the retina, aquariums and Japanese divers. According to him his apparatus should give a perfectly clear picture of submarine depths over which you were swimming while the lead tube gave you sufficient air to breathe.

Even now when, as he does, George sometimes takes me aside to inflict on me a discourse about oxygen intoxication or the advantages of a demand pressure-reducer, I can forget to pay attention to what he is saying, and see instead the George of those days with his big eyes shining beneath a thatch of fair hair, clutching to his chest a dripping gas-mask of Czech army pattern.

George walked back with me to where I lived.

Was I a Scout? Not? That was a pity. He had been a Sea Scout where they had lived before, and he was going to join the local troop though they were not Sea Scouts, which was ridiculous with the sea so close. I told myself that I was going to be a Scout or a Sea Scout, it didn't matter which as long as it was with George, and I determined to talk to my parents about it that very day. We

The apparatus called "Donald" consisted of an old gas mask and a hot-water bottle used as an artificial lung

Testing the first key to the Marvellous Kingdom; the boys ashore worked
the air pump; the swimmer had to enter the water by wading

arranged that the next Sunday we would go to the little cove and try out the mask together.

I took a long time going to sleep that night. Things George had said were running in my mind: "There ought to be star-fish and yellow and mauve sea-anemones, and perhaps white sea-fans deeper down . . . wrecks at the bottom of the sea . . . a Marvellous Kingdom that belongs to no one . . . an unknown Marvellous Kingdom to discover. . . ."

3

I HAD often bathed at that cove and knew it well, but this time we were going to do better than just scratch the surface. In a few minutes the mysterious wonderful world beneath the opaque veil of the surface was going for the first time to reveal some of its secrets to us.

We shouted as we descended the tiers of rock, for we did not yet love the silence.

There were no waves in the cove, scarcely even a gentle lapping. Slowly George started to undress, his eyes fixed on the blue water. I did the same. An almost religious emotion seemed to have taken hold of George and, being his friend, I shared his exaltation. My heart was pounding. George bent forward and speaking softly close to my ear said the words that have now become a sort of password for us, a ritual conjuration to appease the divinities of the sea before diving: "Glaucos the fisherman, son of Thetis and Poseidon, went as he pleased beneath the water . . ."

I had always been fond of mythology and was pleased to see that George shared my taste.

We had agreed that he should try the apparatus first and then lend it to me. It was October and the water was already not as warm as it had been. George dived in in a powder of spray to "savour the sea" as he called it, and for some minutes he swam in and out of the rocks fringing the shore, lithe and supple; then he returned to where I was and emerged gasping and radiant, like a young sea god.

"You aren't the son of Poseidon and Thetis," I said, "but you deserve to be."

"I have my swimming badge, which is the same thing.
. . . Now hand me the apparatus."

I helped him to strap on the hideous snout, and I can
still see his eyes, large and eager behind the big round
glass windows set in the two protuberances of green
rubber. The myth was to be re-enacted. I was so moved
that I pulled his hair as I tightened the webbing straps,
but in the mask he could not say anything; his hands
were already groping and he turned towards the sea.
At last all was ready, slowly he walked into the sea, no
dive this time.

I called: "Is it all right, George?" but he just walked on
without making a sign. Then, when the water was up to
his chest he plunged his face in with the same movement
as with the basin a week before. For some seconds he
remained motionless, as though stupefied, while I kept
calling: "George, is it all right?" But of course with his
ears immersed he could not have heard me.

All at once he came to life, lay on the water and began
to swim. All that I could see was the back of his head and
the lead pipe standing straight up like a submarine
periscope. Slowly, with regular breast strokes George
drew away from the shore and began to round a rocky
islet. Suddenly I could no longer see the lead pipe and I
felt vaguely anxious. Where I had last seen him there was
a little patch of foam. I don't remember exactly whether
I dived in straight away, or whether I waited a moment
or two while I shouted, "George! George!" with a lump
in my throat that kept me from shouting as loudly as I
wanted to. However it was, I was soon swimming
towards the rocky islet.

While I was still several yards away the rubber mask
emerged close to the rock and I exclaimed joyfully:

"All right, George? Coming out now? My turn next."

But the mask submerged again, reappeared and I could see George's hands, two clenched hands trying desperately to tear off the mask that was half full of water. The nails grated on the metal of the buckles. It was those hands that made me realize that George was fighting for his life. The wet straps, of course, would not come out, so, not being able to drag the mask off, George changed his tactics and tried to hoist himself up on to a platform of rock, but being three-parts suffocated already he fell back into the water and disappeared. He reappeared again and miraculously a wave helped him up onto the rock. There he lay tragically still, no longer like Glaucos or Poseidon, or any of the sea gods, but much more like a large stranded fish. A thin stream of water trickled from the lead pipe.

Reaching him at last, I tore off the mask, rather than took it off, and one of the buckles cut his cheek. I shall always remember how George looked at that moment. I have often been afraid since our adventure started, as recently as the day before yesterday when we dived to that wreck, but never, I believe, have I been so petrified as I was then. George was white, his eyes closed, and he was shaken by hiccoughs: then he spat out some salt water and the wound below his eye began to bleed. At last he opened his eyes. I had all the time been calling "George! George!" Now George muttered something unintelligible, then he said quite distinctly:

"Don't be an idiot!"

And immediately afterwards:

"Oh, if only you knew . . ."

That might have applied to the accident, only from the tone in which he said it I was sure it referred to what he had been seeing before the accident.

"Oh, if only you knew!"

Then he said no more, but just looked at me. I shall always remember his face then, for to me he was the very image of adventure lying there with a tiny trickle of salt water coming from his lips, the wound on his cheek, where the buckle of the mask had torn out a small piece of the flesh, but very neatly, leaving a little pink hole from which blood dripped, and his eyes big, eager and enraptured:

"Oh, if only you knew!"

*   *   *

Often now, when camped on this island, before diving to the wreck George and the rest of us have dismantled our breathing apparatus piece by piece, even the delicate on-demand reducing valves, or, as we did to-day, the filter cartridge and the system of oxygen regeneration of a closed-circuit Pirelli helmet. But we were a long way from such things then. Our first accident had brought us up against our first technical problem and this we discussed passionately all the way back. I thought that either a wave must have covered the breathing tube or that George had inadvertently lowered his head too far. But George would not have it. He said that, there being no breakers, a swimmer could not do otherwise than follow the motion of the swell and thus no wave could close the mouth of the breathing tube. He had another explanation for the sudden irruption of the sea, and this was that in following the movements of a large silvery fish he had jerked his head, and so, by its inertia, the heavy lead pipe had pulled the mask out of shape causing part to rise off the skin and it had immediately filled with water.

I ventured to suggest that if that were so, perhaps it would be better to give up the idea of the mask and to try something else. But George was already full of ideas for overcoming what he indulgently called a "small defect".

When I pressed him to tell me the main things that he had seen under the water, he said:

"No, I prefer not to tell you anything; you'll see for yourself."

And then with his great beaming smile:

"The next time I'll let you try the apparatus."

That's George all over.

4

A<small>N</small> hour ago when opening a sea-urchin with Philip's stainless steel dagger I gave my finger and palm a deep gash. George made me dip my hand into a mug of pure alcohol, and then as I was beginning to feel faint, he slapped my face and finally forced three soft toffees into my mouth. When all danger of infection and suffocation was over, George made me an enormous bandage and forbade me to bathe until the cut had closed.

Denied diving, exiled from the sea, I feel a great urge to write, and, rather than wander about among the rocks like a lost soul, I shall take advantage of these two days to continue the story of our adventure. Alone, lying on my stomach in the tent, I can hear the panting of the compressor which is finishing charging our cylinders, and the voices of the others in eager discussion.

Philip is telling Alan the habits of the hermit crab: "You see? The urticating anemone fixed on the shell is an additional protection. Besides, when the shell gets too small they change it, and then they seize the anemone in their pincers and transport it willy-nilly to their new suit of armour. . . ."

George and Claud, the technicians, were talking of the wonderful blending apparatus for breathing they hoped to make one day so as to overcome the narcotic effect of nitrogen. "You would dive with a gadget like the Cousteau narghileh, that would let you get down quickly to 195 feet and enable you to start on only 3 per cent oxygen to 97 per cent hydrogen. No more narcosis. It will be 480 feet for us!"

Then Philip's imperturbable voice: "When it lodges in the inside of a sponge, the hermit crab . . ."

Then Claud again: "And the trials, where will we have those?"

"In the deep off Nice . . ."

It's six years since we began having "trials", but there was never question of any "deep" for those. Our experiments with the old gas mask continued for two months, stopped for the worst of the winter and were resumed again in the spring. But always the water found some crack at the side, got in between the rubber and the skin. Of course the mask was too big for thirteen-year-old George with his thin face and its wide forehead and narrow temples, and each time the trial ended in one or other being half-drowned or suffocated. We were forced to give up.

Meanwhile, a thing that sealed our new friendship. George had taken me to his old friend Rebufat, who lived down near the harbour. Perhaps it was this old man who was the origin of George's keenness; if not, he had certainly done a lot to egg him on: he had been a diver, a sailor, captain of Count don Roy de Ortego's yacht and now, retired, lived modestly surrounded by magnificent models of his own making: galleys, pinnaces, brigs, brigantines, frigates or modern craft which had the smallest little block in its proper place from the deck to the truck of the main mast. There was one big frigate especially, which had all its running gear, halyards, clew-lines, topping-lifts, bowlines, wheel-ropes, sheets, etc.

It became traditional that after admiring the models we ask old Rebufat about the weather, for he was reputed to know all about it. He would go out on to the front step and, standing there, cautiously moisten a finger and hold it up, even if the mistral was blowing with full force, then he would point an index finger at some corner of the heavens:

"There, do you see that little cloud over there?"

" Yes, Mr Rebufat."

"Well. . . . I won't say any more."

Then we would nod our heads and wink as though we understood, and we would go back into his big, light room and sit down round the table. Old Rebufat would push his leather-peaked sailor's cap on to the back of his bald head and his little eyes, the grey colour of foam, would screw up as he told us what we had come to hear: tales of the ghostly wrecks in the great submarine cemeteries, of the gold he had recovered, the dives he had made into the Marvellous Kingdom.

"A fine profession, but a dangerous one, dangerous . . . only the life-line to signal by: one tug, (all right) two tugs, (pump faster) three tugs (too much air); four tugs (pull meup); repeated tugs (danger). Yes, boys, its enthralling but dangerous. It happened once that the sailors, ordinary deckhands, who were pumping started a fight. I am not speaking of to-day. They fought instead of turning the wheel of the crank pump, fought over a woman. So, you see, boys, you must always beware of women, even at sea! And don't forget that. Naturally the diver got no air, and when they fished him up he was quite blue. The sailors were shot, which was only justice, and since then there has always been an officer, armed and sworn-in, to supervise, and those who pump are also divers, not just silly deckhands.

"And then there are the blue-skins, huge muraenas, the octopuses and the poulps. The octopus is larger, but the poulp, well, I can tell you . . . it's more vigorous.

"A dangerous profession, boys, but enthralling and paying too. Two francs leading seaman's pay; three

41

francs fifty bonus for going down, and four francs for each hour under water. You sometimes made fifteen francs a day. That was the life. A fine and a good profession, but dangerous . . .

"Have I ever told you about the time when the pipe had been lying the whole blessed day coiled on the deck plates in the sun and how I was quite overcome with filthy fumes by the time I had got down to five fathoms ?"

"Yes, Mr Rebufat, you told us that and how you pulled the rope, but not as you should have . . ."

"And the time that *Bison* buckled her screw and the engineer wanted to go down to see for himself, as he said?"

"Tell us, Mr Rebufat, tell us. . . ."

*   *   *

It was not only to old Mr Rebufat that George had got me to go with him, but I had also joined the Scout troop so as to be with him. That, however, was not a great success. It all began the day the Scout Master ordered George to remove the Sea Scout badge from his shirt and replace it with that of the ordinary land Scouts. George obeyed grumblingly. As he likes giving orders, I thought that all would be well when he was made second Patrol Leader, but it was not. Rather the contrary. The Patrol Leader was never there and in actual fact it was really George who commanded the Patrol and he did not do it at all to Scout Master Maurice's liking.

The Scout Master really only liked two things: herbariums and well-organized tracking games. George liked only adventure and the sea, and when things were too well-organized they lost half their interest for him. In our patrol there was really only one other who was a kindred spirit, a boy whose real name was Philip, though

42

we called him Matto-Grosso and later Spider-crab, a tall
skinny chap with the air of a young buccaneer, magnificently ignorant of the names of the departments of
France, but infallible on anything to do with Colonel
Fawcett and his last journey, and could spend half an
hour dreaming over a map of the unexplored Amazon
basin.

The others in the patrol are scarcely worth mentioning:
little worms who could not swim and refused to learn,
and got the jitters in three feet of water, but who were
open-mouthed with admiration of the Scout Master when
at the evening meetings he imitated the cry of the Spirit
of the Forest, and were capable of spending a whole day
following the warpath with the astuteness of young Sioux,
the only part of them to be seen above the tall ferns being
their large behinds covered with blue serge.

Thus George, Philip and I began to form a little clan of
three of our own. George told us of weird projects, plans
for strange apparatus, vitreous pouches, cowls or bells
that would allow him to immerse himself again in the
waters of the little cove, and see the big silver fish that had
made him turn his head so abruptly; the submerged rocks,
the motionless algae, and the light that came from
nowhere . . . all that fairyland of which George was
unable to give us any idea by describing it, but which we
glimpsed in the brightness of his shining eyes as he spoke
of it.

Philip, who was out for big game, asked anxiously:

"Will there be a gun in the equipment?"

"Yes, there'll be a gun."

"And we'll go down into places where no one,
absolutely no one, has gone before?"

"Of course. We'll be the first. Places more magnificently
virgin than the heart of Matto Grosso . . ."

43

That lit in Philip's eyes the flame of conquest, a little cruel perhaps, but it has never gone out since.

But the apparatus had still to be built, and none of us had the cash for anything so expensive.

We seldom talked of our plans at the Scout hall. It was not that we were afraid of our secrets being discovered, but just that there was not the right atmosphere there. Philip having been accepted by old Mr Rebufat, his little house became our favourite meeting place. How different it was there to the Scout hall: models, finished or still being made, taking the place of shields and cardboard banderoles; the room smelt of tar, sea, "Treasure Island" and adventure with a capital A; adventure a thousand times more adventurous than any possible adventure on land that man organized.

"Have I ever told you the story, boys, of the master-at-arms who cut off his own head with a boarding axe?"

"Yes, Mr Rebufat, you told us that last Sunday."

"And what happened to the divers who, in 1913, recovered 300 cases of brandy from the *Melpomene*, sunk in 16 fathoms on a rocky bottom?"

"Yes, Mr Rebufat, you have told us that too."

"And about the boy called Yawl, a little sponge diver in the Red Sea, who at the age of fourteen found Pharaoh's treasure on the bottom and became king of his tribe, but then gave up his crown to go on diving and died at the age of sixteen, eaten by a shark?"

"No, Mr Rebufat, we've never heard about that. Tell us."

*   *   *

Things became strained between George and Scout Master Maurice during the Easter holidays which brought the first of the fine weather.

There was to be a great rally and, of course, tracking games. The patrols were ordered to make their way to the end of the Saint-Césaire peninsula without using the road which was supposed to be guarded by Cruel Hawk's men.

In the woods the Scout Master had laid ambushes and prepared terrible tests: leaves that you had to identify before you could go on and some of which were supposed to be poisonous, weird knots to be tied with your eyes shut, one being a simple bowline round your body which you had to tie with one hand, "as if you were being swept away by the current", the current being an assistant pulling on the free end.

The idea must have come to George the moment he heard the details of the game:

"All routes are allowed except the road; you did say all?" and the Scout Leader replied categorically: "Absolutely all."

No doubt he was counting on catching us, copse or no copse, at the point where the tongue of land is narrowest, but there was a smile on George's face.

It was a great day for us three novices who, with faces as pale as white flags, had our first day at sea. It was a great day for Philip who already saw himself scudding towards new worlds; a great day for George who (on purpose) let his hat be blown away and replaced it with his old Sea Scouts cap which he had, suspiciously, handy, and a great day, too, for old Mr Rebufat who had come with us as skipper and who seemed to think himself twenty years younger.

"Yes, boys, the day I laid the Count's yacht alongside at Monaco; it was so beautifully done that even the English applauded."

It was a great day for me too, for I was at the tiller alone for two hours; and a great day for Scout Master Maurice who came to rallying point at nightfall having vainly waited for us, glasses glued to his eyes, and camouflaged like Buffalo Bill, while we, under the guidance, first of Mr Rebufat, and then of George alone, were tacking across the blue sea, more or less under his nose.

He took it very well and admitted defeat. The next day, however, George had to go and buy a new Scout hat, which infuriated him.

5

WE were still without the means to penetrate into our Marvellous Kingdom and had to content ourselves with the enthralling stories of old Mr Rebufat about such things as how the muraena "turns over on the starboard side" before it seizes its prey, or how the best way to cook a "pourpre" without it getting tough is by immersing it very slowly on the end of a string so that the water never goes off the boil.

Every Thursday, as soon as we could get away from the Scout meeting, we would stroll down to the harbour. And yet we did not like the harbour. The water was dirty and had gaudy splodges of reflected paint and patches of fuel oil and coal dust; and always there was the grating noise of the cranes, always there were men with hollow cheeks and dull eyes, men who were not in the least like old Mr Rebufat, and who shouted indistinct words at us as we passed with our scarves and khaki shorts.

But, as on the evening of that first Sunday, we always returned to the harbour as being the gateway to the sea. Beyond that sordid, noisy threshold we imagined the great silent adventure, the moving surface that man calls the sea and which is in fact but the frontier to the real sea, the deep sea, the sea into which you plunge, which covers you and welcomes you. After all the harbour with its dull water and its rotting boats tied up for ever was more worth-while than the herbariums and tracking of the Scout Leader, whose tracks never ran along the sea.

On our way back from the docks or the naval basin we would stop to look into certain shopwindows. Two especially drew us irresistibly, that of a ship's chandler's called, "At the sign of the Navigator's Light", and that of the "Old Portolano Bookshop". We would stand for ages, noses flattened against the glass of the ship's chandler's, gazing ecstatically at a sextant, marine glasses and a Scott projector, enough to furnish the setting for our dreams.

We were able to go farther at the bookshop, where we knew the owner. He let us look through his reproductions of seascapes and old engravings showing the uniforms of a hundred years ago: beardless cadets wearing a thick black cravat beneath their blue collars, young apprentices wearing large straw hats with two large ribbands trailing behind, midshipmen with little hats and long hair, and one that especially impressed us, a picture of "Ensign Gaspard-Emmanuel de Farsac, born 31 September 1839 —on board *Semillante*". At the time of the famous wreck on the rocks off the islands of Lavezzi he must have been fifteen. Perhaps he was a friend of the little cabin-boy with the wide-opened eyes whom Daudet mentions in *Les Lettres de mon Moulin*?

Thus, as well as all the bearded seadogs there was a good sprinkling of youth to be found in those dusty old boxes. A hundred years ago you left school early and boys were still young when they learned to fight and to die honourably. We were the unresisting victims of their fascination, and to us their young faces were both a temptation and a reproach. When would we at last be able to take part in our adventure and risk our lives?

George comforted us. Sooner or later we would succeed; we were young and the future belonged to us.

Before we could bring ourselves to leave the harbour we would go back for a last look at the ship's chandler's, which would be shut: the copper-sheathed wheel would be no longer turning, the compass in its gimbals fixed on a fictitious course, the white, green and red of the thick glass of the navigation lights dull and lifeless, though one day they would shine out. In the middle of that window, like a crown among lesser treasures, lay a diver's helmet complete with collar, adjustable valve, and thick glass behind the grills over the eyepieces—and what visions they were going to see.

Towards the end of that winter George read an article about British frogmen and the Italian "human torpedoes" straddled by two "nuatatori" equipped with autonomous diving suits. The article told of amazing adventures: how in the middle of the night the submarine surfaced and the men, dressed in rubber, emerged from the conning-tower which closed again behind them. Then the valves were opened and the submarine submerged again, with the divers clinging to the handrail.

Down went the submarine, the plates of its super-structure covered with an ascending stream of bubbles, down until it landed on the sandy bottom, swayed, and was still.

Then the divers, hampered by their rubber armour, pressed and squeezed beneath the pressure, pulled their torpedoes from their protective covers, the mounts astride which they were to go and destroy Gibraltar.

Guided by their luminous watertight compasses the teams made towards their objectives, or went up to get a sight from the surface, only their heads emerging from the short waves.

Their equipment, however, was not perfect. Their breathing masks were always failing and forcing them, suddenly suffocating, to escape full speed for the surface; or else the torpedoes became heavy and nose-dived leaving their riders helpless on the surface.

49

One of them, however, the most fortunate, got across the net, round the mole and into the roads, only to break down less than fifty yards from the dark silhouette, large funnel, tripod mast, and four large double turrets of the cruiser *Barham*. Walking laboriously on the bottom, the Italian officer hauled the torpedo towards the enormous hull with its barnacles and shells . . .

Thirty-two thousand tons of metal, eight fifteen-inch guns, twelve hundred men—at the mercy of one officer.

The article was stuffed with technical details, the salient features of the engines used, filter cartridges of soda lime to eliminate the carbon dioxide, a bottle of oxygen to regenerate the mixture they breathed, the possible accidents, oxygen intoxication, asphyxiation by carbon dioxide, pulmonary over-pressure, shallow-water blackout, etc.

After that neither Philip nor I saw George for a week. That week of solitary cogitation gave birth to the apparatus which was to go down in George's personal archives as the Baby's Bottle. It was called that because you breathed in your air not in the mask, but through a mouthpiece like a teat. Also, although he denied it fiercely later, George intended the name to indicate how sure and easy the apparatus would be to use.

I cannot think of the Baby's Bottle without shuddering. There was a respirator shaped like an U and made of a car's inner tube with the two ends sealed with rubber solution. In the centre of the U was an old tin communicating with the rubber tube by means of wired tubes and serving as a filter. Inside it George had made a series of compartments of meat-safe mesh between which were layers of soda lime. A flexible rubber tube led from the top of the filter-tin and, when the contraption was strapped on your chest, ended "quite naturally", as

George put it, at your mouth. Your nose was clamped in a clothes-peg, and a pair of motoring goggles made watertight with adhesive plaster protected your eyes and allowed you to see perfectly, or so George said. The problem of oxygen regeneration, being too complicated to solve, had been deliberately disregarded, George explaining with terrifying calm that it would be enough to dive fairly quickly. As the pressure increased, the percentage of oxygen required would diminish as the actual quantity of air absorbed at each respiration increased. George maintained a prudent silence over what happened when you went up again. A belt, to which 20 lb. of lead piping were tied with string, completed the equipment.

George kept Philip and me back after one Scout meeting and triumphantly showed us the design of Baby's Bottle most carefully drawn on a double sheet of squared paper. It appeared that we already possessed the inner tube, the tin, the clothes peg and the motoring goggles (George's father's) and that we would have to renew the adhesive tape after each dive. We still needed the wired-tubing and the lock-nuts, the meat-safe mesh and the soda lime, and, as far as George could estimate, all that would cost 14s. 9d. George possessed 2s. 4d, my savings, which I at once offered, amounted to 1s. 9d; and when Philip had turned out his pockets he could find only 3d. To excuse himself he told us that his mother's birthday had been only a week before. That, however, did not alter the fact that we were still far from our goal. Nor could we raid the patrol's funds, for all expenditure had to be authorized by the Scout Master and he would only allow the acquisition of cooking materials. At a stretch we might have put in for a tin of something suitable, but we already had that.

After considerable discussion George put forward a

suggestion: why not seek other shareholders to supply the missing funds and thereby acquire the right to participate in our experiments?

After much hesitation we agree that a suitable person would be Claud Walter, son of the proprietor of the Grand Garage. He was not a member of the troop, but was a grand fellow, very ingenious, always pottering in his father's workshops and usually well in funds, which was certainly no drawback for what we were trying to do.

Philip undertook to recruit him.

*　　*　　*

I shall always remember that first meeting, which took place on George's birthday. It was very impressive, with all of us gathered round the table and George in the chair (the only one). It was a cross between a board meeting and a masonic reunion.

The first thing to be done was to find a name for our association. Philip proposed "Expedition for the Exploration of Submarine Depths and their Fauna", but that seemed a bit too long and also an expedition was essentially a temporary affair, while ours was to be a lasting association intended to make lengthy experiments.

I suggested "Brotherhood of the Friends of the Marvellous Kingdom", but Philip protested; it was too sibylline, smacked too much of the secret society. In the end our new recruit, Claud, put forward his idea, "Centre for Experiments in Submarine Apparatus, Respiratory", or C.E.S.A.R. for short. That was both striking and easy to remember. ("Later, when we start selling the apparatus, its publicity value will be very useful.")

To me that was far too technical, and I much preferred Philip's suggestion with its smell of adventure and discovery.

George said nothing, just looked at us inquiringly as we made our suggestions. I would have liked it better if he had deigned to suggest something himself. I should probably have been able to deduce from it something of how he regarded our adventure. When in the end he did speak, it was to support Claud. To begin with at any rate the technical side would be more important than the exploration as such. Yes, indeed—Claud was right. C.E.S.A.R would answer perfectly.

Claud's eyes glowed with pride behind his steel-rimmed glasses. He sat up straight on his stool, and beneath his mop of red hair his freckled face split into a grin of triumph. He was George's for ever.

Thus was CESAR, a company strictly limited to its initial capital of 14s. 9d. founded.

"And now the plans for the apparatus."

George and Claud discussed them at length. They were obviously the Society's technicians. Yes, Claud could provide the wired-tubing. He would himself make the necessary modifications to some he could get in his father's garage. But he thought the shape of the mouthpiece ought to be changed to make it easier to manufacture.

Unintentionally I poured cold water on the project by asking:

"Have you shown the plans to Mr Rebufat?"

George hesitated slightly before replying:

"Yes, and he said that it wouldn't work, but," he added lightly, "you know what these professionals are, once out of their copper diving-helmets and lead-soled boots and they won't hear of anything else . . ."

Claud was thinking:

"All the same it might be wise to provide a release mechanism for the weighted belt . . ."

George raised his hand in protest: as far as he was

concerned, he was not afraid of that being necessary, but, perhaps, it might all the same. . . .

That evening clinched it. We none of us realized then on what an adventure we were embarking, nor that it would lead us to this little desert island where we are camped now above the wreck, the haunt of octopuses, muraenas and all the wizards of the sea, above enchanted valleys capped with blue water and carpeted with live flowers, a world of caves with mysterious moving lights and great fairy castles full of shadows and sparkle, whose towers we can scale in a few seconds with a slight kick of our feet.

We have conquered it now, that marvellous kingdom that is so quiet and still, so far from noisy man, from the wind that blows and the light that casts shadows.

And for all its ugly title our daring brotherhood has prospered, we have founded a sort of Order of Brethren of the Sea. . . .

"Well", said George, "that disposes of the technical matters. Let us now celebrate my fourteenth birthday by eating some cake."

It took almost a month to make the Baby's Bottle. Without Claud's help it would have been very much longer. Naturally George was the one to test it out first.

The day of the first trial was grey and rather dreary with a slight swell coming into the cove. It did not look as though visibility would be very good as we stood round George while he slowly undressed. Then carefully I strapped the weird apparatus on to his chest, Claud having first checked over every part. George shivered at the touch of the cold metal; then he adjusted the watertight goggles and took the rubber-coated pipe between his teeth. Claud then inflated the air-bag with a bicycle pump. I buckled the weighted belt round George's waist, then heavily he walked into the sea and at the very last moment, clipped the clothes peg on to his nose. He must have been pretty exactly weighted, because for several seconds I could see his fair head drifting like a buoy alongside the rocks, then a short wave fell on it and submerged it. Then there was nothing to be seen. I imagined George six or ten feet below the surface, drowning, a ghastly phantom floating under the green water, his hair waving like pallid seaweed. I longed to be helping him.

A minute and a half passed and then George's hands appeared, caught hold of the rock. Suffocating, George hoisted himself up, removed the teat from his mouth and breathed in great draughts of air.

"It's not altogether right," he groaned.

One of the halves of the "watertight" goggles was full of water, the other half-full. George was gasping and his heart pounding like a hammer.

"What did you see? It's my turn! Me next!" cried Philip, who feared neither man nor devil.

George shook his head: no! Then he dropped to his knees on the sharp rock. Quickly we relieved him of the apparatus.

"My turn now," said Philip, less boldly.

But George again shook his head.

Claud, puzzled, was fingering the apparatus. His forehead wrinkled. He had opened the tin and removed from the outside of the filter a few grains of lime.

We went back home in silence, the Baby's Bottle tied with string to the luggage-carrier on George's bicycle, where it dripped mournfully. At the gate of George's house we shook hands and split up.

I kept thinking of George all through dinner. He must have been feeling pretty depressed and discouraged. Perhaps he was thinking that we would leave him in the lurch, drop him and his inaccessible kingdom. I bolted my sweet and hurried to Philip whom I found in the badly lit courtyard of the building where he lived, holding a large struggling rabbit by the ears.

"You can kill them with a blow on the back of the head or break their necks by pulling on the ears and feet at the same time."

His teeth shone white in the shadows. He seemed both proud of his knowledge and slightly ashamed.

"Kill it whichever way you like, but do it quickly and join me at George's," I said.

A number 19 tram put me down opposite the Walters', and Claud's big sister answered the door. She was just like Claud, except that she had pigtails, red ones that waggled when she leaned forward to tell me from the top of the steps that Claud had already gone out.

I caught him up just before we got to George's and we gave each other a conspiratorial smile. Philip arrived a few minutes later, the murder of his rabbit already weighing on his conscience.

I no longer remember exactly what we said to George, but I do remember his reply: he said that at least the Baby's Bottle had done him the service of showing him how strong our friendship was. He knew now that we were a team that could never be split nor conquered. And I remember his triumphant smile as he said that.

From that moment we all felt quite certain that with George we would realize our great dream and that sooner or later the Marvellous Kingdom would be ours.

6

IT was on the Monday that things went wrong for George, though only temporarily. As I mounted the steps to George's house, I met Scout Master Maurice coming out. He gave me a good-day so curt as to be slightly ominous. The moment I got inside I realized that I had come at quite the wrong moment.

"George, come down and bring the cane!"

At the foot of the stairs, face upturned towards the upper storeys, stood George's father pawing the ground in a state of frenzy like an Achilles demanding a sword and Trojans to kill after the death of Patrocles. It was obvious whom George took after. Monsieur Rougemont, fair-haired and big, like a Scandinavian warrior, possessed an explosive force comparable to that of his only son. This only son of his seemed to be in no hurry to appear and bring his father the cane for which the latter persisted in calling with ominous insistence. My arrival caused a diversion.

"Come in. It's quite a good thing you're here, since you're one of the band. Your Scout Master has just told me everything. You're both the victim and the accomplice of my son. He'll end by killing himself with his ridiculous experiments and you with him. You shall see how one treats such boys and I can only hope that your father will deal with you similarly."

I might have told him that my father was a sea-captain and at that moment in either the Red Sea or the Indian Ocean, but, instead, I exclaimed:

"George is innocent, Sir, quite innocent, and . . ."

As an intervention it was neither clever nor tactful.

"Oh! George is innocent is he? You presume to tell me what I ought to do! Very well, you shall see how one chastises innocents like him. I am sorry that you are not my son."

I had no regrets on that score.

At last the "innocent" one deigned to descend the stairs holding the cane discreetly behind his back. On the bottom step, stammering and shifting from one foot to the other, he produced some sort of explanation of which all I could make out was the words "sea-urchin" and "scientific interest". As an argument it was manifestly too slight to make his father modify his views in any way.

Now, at the distance of five years, it is easy to joke about it, and George himself laughed the other day when we recalled the somewhat ridiculous scene of the well-applied thrashing he received. But I remember that at the time I would very gladly not have been there. My heart was pounding. I was fearfully embarassed for George. And secretly I was awfully afraid that he might ruin everything by struggling or blubbing like some common school kid who has been caught out. It seemed to me too that my being there added to his shame, and I was afraid that he would hold the additional humiliation I was unwittingly causing him against me, and that hence-forward there would be an insurmountable constraint between us.

George's father was growing impatient.

"Come along, quickly now."

I do not know how George would have behaved if I had not been there, but as it was he gave me a reassuring smile and with sudden stoicism handed his father the cane with a hand that was perfectly steady. I felt a great wave of relief. George was rising to the occasion and would retain all his prestige intact. And he had smiled to me, so he didn't mind me being there.

Monsieur Rougemont, however, appeared quite un-impressed by the Roman bearing of his son whom he now seized and thrusting his head under his left arm, held him thus. For a moment I thought of trying to intervene again, but I was afraid that to do that might merely aggravate the punishment poor George was about to receive. Instead, I turned my back and looked at the wall.

There was a pause of a few seconds, then a whistle, a dull thud and a strangled yelp. To use one of George's expressions, the explanation was short but violent. When it was finished and I looked round, George was buckling his belt again with feigned detachment; his eyes avoided mine, his lips were trembling slightly and he was rubbing his nose frantically in an attempt to keep back two tears that trembled on his lashes. Then he decided to wink an eye in my direction and that dislodged a tear.

Calmer now, George's father asked in a more normal tone of voice:

"Will you do any more of it?"

A gasp from George:

"Of course—I will."

A whistle as George's father flourished the cane.

"You want to show off before your friend, but remember that I can do more of this too."

George glanced at the cane and prudently said nothing. Then a disarming smile appeared on his face, and he said:

"Anyway, I don't see how you can blame me; you did worse when you were a boy."

That took the wind out of Monsieur Rougemont's sails. Poor George, I thought, he won't be able to sit down for a week.

"What did I do that was worse?"

Speaking very quickly and well aware of his peril, George said:

"When you were fourteen you went off to sea for five days, alone in a little cutter. Was that any better?"

"How do you know that story?"

George was recovering his assurance.

"You told it me yourself when I was seven and it didn't matter then if I did know it."

George's father was a good loser and now it was his turn to smile:

"Well, yes, perhaps. But I would have you know, young rascal, that the consequences were identical. I can still remember the beating your grandfather gave me. He had a strong arm and I must admit that I unrestrainedly cried for mercy."

George cut a wry face:

"I wouldn't call your arm weak either."

George's father laughed, quite won over.

"George, no ill-will?"

"None at all. I deserved it. I ought not to have kept anything from you. Only admit that your adventure with the cutter was as bad as mine . . ."

"Granted, granted."

Monsieur Rougemont's eyes were dancing. Shamelessly he got rid of the cane by handing it to me.

"Yes, she was a magnificent cutter. It was a magnificent piece of disobedience, a magnificent joy-ride and a magnificent beating. Come on back to my study. George, go to the dining-room and get a bottle of aperitif and glasses, your friend's quite pale. Since your mother's not here, I'll tell you about it, but don't you let her know that I have. The cutter was called *Saint Francois* like the one in the song and, you see, my uncle was with the Mediterranean Dockyards . . .

George, sitting most peculiarly in his chair, shifted uneasily, yet there was a glow of affection in his eyes as he watched his father, but he realized the comical side to it all.

Afterwards, without quite knowing how it had happened, we found ourselves speaking of our plans, of the Marvellous Kingdom and of all that we had done until this unsolicited intervention on the part of our too-conscientious Scout Master. George's father was now angry with him for having made him chastise his son so vigorously and in public.

"I could see at once that he wasn't very intelligent", he told us. "How I wish I were your age and able to go diving with you! I can certainly see how enthralling it must be."

*　　　*　　　*

George walked home with me.

"I'm pleased", he said.

"About what?"

"About Dad ending up by, how shall I put it", George swallowed, "by taking it so well."

"Does it hurt?" I asked affectionately, changing the subject.

"Not at all, not in the least", George assured me.

"And another thing, when you told your father that you didn't bear him any ill-will and that you had deserved it, did you really think that or did you just say it to smooth things over? You don't need to answer that, if you don't want to."

"Of course I thought it. He was right. He's a vigorous type, my father. You know something of what he dared do when he was fourteen."

"All the same, the Scout Master could have kept his mouth shut."

"He meant well, and it has turned out all right. And while on the subject, I don't mind you, but not a word to the others. I don't really want the entire Troop to know that I've had a thrashing. I don't mind you knowing", he said again. "In future I'll tell you everything."

We looked each other in the face, eyes shining, and understood that our friendship had taken a definite step forward, that the barriers between us had been torn down by the events of that afternoon. Later, far beneath the sea, in the icy corridors of submarine grottoes, we were to know other agonizing minutes when we clenched our teeth to keep them from chattering with fear, long seconds when we could get no air, and were distracted and panic-stricken. It was impossible to dissemble and keep such feelings from the other. The ups-and-downs of our adventure revealed us to each other, left us without false humility in triumph and without pride in defeat, left us transparent and ready to admit to each other our secret triumphs and our failures.

"That's a promise, not a word to the others?" George insisted.

"Of course, naturally. Although you've nothing to hide, for you behaved darned well, like a proper young Spartan before the altar of Artemis."

"Pity that we lacked the lovely Artemis. If you like, I'll lend you Talbot's translation of Plutarch's *Life of Lycurgus*. . . . Good night!"

7

It was Sunday and George was standing, facing the sea, reading the morning service as he did each day. The wind from the sea fluttered the thin pages under his fingers, but for me the familiar words evoked other pictures, transported me beyond the sea. The old ladies would be entering the dim doorway of the church for the first office which would be about to begin at the little altar twinkling like an oasis of light. The sacristan would bring the altar-cruets, the choir boy make his genuflection; there would be whisperings and the scrape of chairs. The peace of the community; surely there is the true happiness; only I was afraid that it was unattainable for us, that we could only know it to the extent to which we were deprived of it. We could not be happy except with a violent, fleeting, fragile happiness. But did it matter what the future held in store for us? This second camp on that uninhabited islet would always be for us a peak, and no deception, no solitude could cheat us of those weeks of taking risks, and of conquering. Never had we felt so close to our Maker. With each dive we seemed to be putting our lives in His hands and receiving in exchange enthralling confidences about the most mysterious and varied part of His creation. Reading the Book of Job almost brought a malicious little conspiratorial smile to our lips:

"Hast thou entered into the springs of the sea? or hast thou walked in the search of the depth?"

Five years ago we did not see so far and we made fun

of the Book of Job, but we did have an inkling that the Marvellous Kingdom was a gift from God and that as Scouts we would be at home there. Actually I have never really known what brought things to a head at that Whitsun crisis, for George does not like talking of that period of our lives, but as far as I can judge now, in the light of what has happened since, it was not just stupid vanity that made George want to attract special attention to his patrol or to himself. Ever after that, he dreamed of planting our emblem in the heart of that unexplored and Marvellous Kingdom, and little flashes of revolt would come into his eyes when he saw people like Philip reduced to playing at explorers and following in the tracks of Scout Master Maurice's great boots through spinneys strewn with sandwich paper, when so close, just a few yards lower down, was the most marvellous and least explored of all jungles.

But nobody seemed to believe. The Scout Master and other "realistic" grown-ups, except perhaps George's father, refused to take our dreams seriously and even laughed at us.

*　　*　　*

We were to have a camp fire on Midsummer's Eve. George had asked that we should have it by the sea, on the beach of the little creek, where he wanted to organize a nautical game with his Elk Troop, but the Scout Master had refused. The sea in June was both dangerous and alarming. The fire was to be well inland. Although George had never said as much, I felt that his request had been a sort of test, a last and rather pathetic attempt to overcome the barrier between them without disrupting or renouncing anything, and that the Scout Master's refusal had acted as a finger-post that hastened George's decision to make a break.

George trying new apparatus: it consisted of a large metal box open at the bottom and a telephone was fitted within it

Submarine Scouts under instruction with modern apparatus

The Scout Master was really a perfectly good fellow, but he was a landlubber and earthbound. Behind him he had generations of ancestors who had driven ploughs, sown and planted, lived by the land and for the land, thought only of the land. He had both feet firmly fixed on the ground, and to know him it was enough to see him gently crumbling some earth between his fingers.

One day, in an attempt to win him over, George had taken him an enormous mauve anemone in a bucket of salt water, the largest anemone I have ever seen.

"There, a present for you."

The Scout Master had bent down, a gleam of interest in his eye.

"That's pretty! Is it really an animal?"

Then he had turned away again, no longer interested.

"So much the worse, it would decay soon."

"Exactly", said George. "That makes it even more lovely."

But it had not achieved its effect.

Our Scout Master did not bother about unknown worlds and creatures, and to have rid himself of his weight, as we now did every day, to breathe air at a pressure of six pounds and violate the forbidden solitudes of wrecks, would have seemed to him, as to his farmer ancestors, useless, dangerous and even slightly sacrilegious, as though it were violating a retreat that God had not given us. We, however, were not aware of our ancestors; each time we dived we felt magnificently free of any inheritance, we felt ourselves the first, the start of a new race, as, say, at the beginning of the world, rich in our one new experience in a new world, where our age-old reflexes are ineffective, ridiculous and dangerous.

Yes, now that our adventure is at its height, now that the Marvellous Kingdom has been conquered, I am more than ever convinced that we had to make the break and that George was right to search on his own, with just his few contemporaries, for our way beneath the waters.

* * *

I had decided to follow George and so had Philip. On the evening of the break we found ourselves in the intimate atmosphere of the chaplain's room with its familiar objects and the Pieta of Maurice Denis on the wall. The Scout Master was to have come, but he had not yet arrived. Perhaps he wanted to give the chaplain time to win us round. The chaplain sat as his desk talking of indifferent matters, but his voice was quiet and restful. I imagined that he perhaps would understand us.

"So you really want to chuck it?"

Now it had come. There was a painful silence. But George is pretty shrewd and not afraid of tacking among the rocks of diplomacy. No, this was not a question that concerned the chaplain. We were not wishing to leave because of anything to do with the requirements of the Scout ideal, it was solely a question of Scout activities, of the choice of means for arriving at this ideal, thus a question that concerned the Scout Master alone. Whatever happened we would remain faithful to our Promise. The chaplain raised his hand in a gesture that perhaps meant that all problems were linked and therefore concerned him, or implied doubt of our being able to remain faithful once outside the fraternity.

But George had no fears on this score. He looked at the chaplain in such a way that the latter never put his doubts into words. George pressed his advantage home.

"We also have our adventure, and if we agreed to give it up when we feel called to pursue it, we would then be failing to keep our promise."

66

The chaplain said nothing. He was thinking, his head in his hands.

Then the Scout Master arrived.

"George is crazy. This business of submarine diving doesn't make sense. And anyway I should like to know what your parents think of it?"

George blushed furiously, then forced himself to smile: "I had a very thorough talk with my father. We threshed the whole matter out (here he looked at me) and it is all now open and above board."

The Scout Master made a little dubious grimace: Even so, what had George achieved. It was just a craze. What was the point of diving among fish? The whole thing must stop, and the sooner the better.

That was the end. There was no going back after that. George clenched his teeth and said no more. His face wore the obstinate look it had on his bad days, and the little scar left by the wound the mask had made was strangely red on his pale cheek. The Scout Master apparently had no more liking for dreams than for anemones; he liked tangible things, things that lasted and had lasted. In the game we were playing that day there was no possibility of beating to windward under the Scout Master's nose as we had on that famous occasion.

The Scout Master left without shaking hands. We felt that if it had not been for the chaplain he would have slammed the door.

Then the chaplain spoke, as calm as ever, his voice, a voice that seemed to question everything:

"Then you wish to leave?"

He no longer said "chuck it" or even give it up, as he had at the beginning, and George seized upon that.

" Yes, Father, if we don't go now, we'll let them down later on."

I could hear the Scout Master pacing the corridor outside, presumably waiting.

"Come here, the three of you; I'll give you my benediction", said the chaplain.

*   *   *

The days that followed were painful ones. Certain Scouts avoided us, others ostentatiously offered us their right hands, whereas it had been our Scout custom to shake with our left hands. On our shirts, which we continued to wear, were darker patches showing where a badge had been removed. We felt as though we had been degraded.

We had forgotten all the puerilities of the Troop and remembered only the camp fires and the nights spent under the stars and the wakings at dawn in the hot days of summer. Philip, I remember, quite deserted the harbour to make a regular Thursday visit to one or other of the places where the Troop had been, trailing Claud along with him: "Here, you see, last year we had a great Scout game, an awful flop. . ."

One evening after dinner I went into George's room without knocking and found him staring fixedly at the Sea Scout cap he had had at Brest. He blushed redder than I had ever seen him and looked very ashamed, till I told him that the other evening I had spent hours poring over my album of photographs from our Scout camps. After that we told each other that we weren't going to be sentimental any more.

I am afraid that only Scouts, or those who have been Scouts, will understand how we felt. It was a sort of grief, not a childish grief, but perhaps our first grief as men. The community had rejected us and our brethren turned from us; yet I believe that all three of us found in that a certain secret pleasure, which was largely made up of pride at having made such a decision, the intoxication of the break with the security of the group, and the joy of setting off on an adventure made more risky by our being on our own. Also, perhaps, there was a certain bitter pleasure in being able to say to the others: "You don't believe in us, you condemn us now, but you'll see . . . it's we who are right, and while you play, we shall be risking our lives as pioneers . . ." Then, too, we remembered the benediction the chaplain had given us and we thought of the future.

*   *   *

Later, said George, when God shall have granted us material success, we will found an Order in some ancient castle on the coast. We will live in the sea, for God who created the sea. The chapel will be dedicated to St. Francis and we will carve fish on the capitals of the pillars in the cloisters, as the early Christians did. At the very foot of the cliff, ten fathoms under the water, we will have our oratory, our inviolable temple, and every day we will deck it afresh with live flowers.

"First, we must succeed", said Philip, "but with you we will."

*   *   *

What astonishes me most about our adventure is just this confidence that we had, our unwavering trust in George despite criticism, remonstrances and the mockery of which plenty came our way, despite even the regrettable set-backs that inevitably accompanied our early experiments. That we persevered and retained our trust is all the more surprising because such virtues were not really characteristic of us, but an exceptional outcome of circumstances to which we would otherwise have reacted with discouragement and inconstancy.

I am not going to give a complete list of all the experiments, some both dangerous and ridiculous, that marked our progression from the Czech gas-mask to our final success. Since then of course we have known of the existence of diving apparatus that would have enabled us to penetrate the world of our dreams, but these have all been beyond our reach, from the copper helmet to the independent diving suit with which we dive to-day, and we were compelled to start from scratch, to reconstruct it all on our own level, that of people without either lathe, drilling-machine or high-pressure bottle, but just hammer, punch, cold chisel and bicycle pump. Ours were clumsy efforts which unwittingly followed, often gropingly and inadequately, in the footsteps of unknown men who throughout the centuries had themselves dreamed of the Marvellous Kingdom.

There are plenty of boys who will be able to see themselves doing what we did. Who has not been left day-dreaming by *Twenty Thousand Leagues Under The Sea*? Who has ever halted in front of an aquarium and not felt vague stirrings and longings prompted by the motionless lightness of the fish? How many have not drawn, at any rate in secret and just for themselves, the design of some apparatus that would permit them to realize this eternal dream, something to link them with the surface, a pliant tube of some kind attached to a sort of float?

Our only merit was that we persevered, but that was due to George and his desperate eagerness. He, after all, had had a glimpse of the Marvellous Kingdom; and when we doubted or hesitated, it was enough for him to remind us of that first dive and the great silver fish that had made him turn his head so abruptly that the mask had filled in an instant.

On other occasions we would go to the cove, and if it

was very fine we would make out the bottom, the dark patches of the rocks, the sand that we were sure was finer than that of the beach, the motionless grass of the meadows on which we would so dearly have loved to lie. Sometimes there would be vague gleams down below and Philip's eyes would light up. He seemed to know it all already in imagination or in memory, and perhaps what impelled us to seek our way beneath the waters was a mysterious sort of nostalgia, rather than any avidity for the unknown.

And now, when we can glide along above all these splendours that we promised ourselves, our feelings are less those of having penetrated into forbidden territory than of having been relieved of our mortal weight and rediscovered a lost paradise of which we had once more become worthy.

8

We had to wait two years for our first success, which took the form of a weird apparatus which the incorrigible George called "Donald". We never dared admit that it had taken us two years to conceive and perfect anything so simple, for Donald was a gas-mask (the same old one) connected to a rubber pouch, an old hot-water bottle, which we pompously called an "artificial lung" or "respiratory bag". Instead of trying to regenerate the air in the hot-water bottle by chemical means, we just renewed it by means of a long tube reaching to the surface and attached to a hand-pump supplied by Claud. Such a system, which let the diver breathe air at the pressure of his surroundings, seemed to us to have all the necessary qualities. If the bag became excessively distended, the surplus air escaped quite simply by the rim of the mask.

Having learned prudence, we made the first experiments in a bath. George spent twenty minutes lying on his back under water while Philip, Claud and I took it in turns to pump. Then George suddenly shot out like a flying fish and, still in the mask, ran all over the house uttering cries of triumph, while I ran after him brandishing the pump to which he was still attached by five yards of dripping pipe. Having assembled both his parents and the cook George again demonstrated the success of our invention. George's father appeared most interested. Perhaps he was, or perhaps he just wanted to emphasize that his attitude had changed since the incident with the cane. After that Philip, Claud and I took it in turn to try the apparatus. When he removed the mask Philip passed a remark that has become for us both a password and a sort of incantation to avert bad luck:

"You breathe better down there than at the top of the Eiffel Tower," he said.

I got in after Philip, and slowly let myself down on my back. All at the once the tepid water swept across the two eyepieces. Through the rippled surface of the water I could see George leaning over the bath, a huge smile on his face and the light of triumph in his eyes. When I exhaled, the mask became unstuck from my face in order to let the air out and I had the disagreable feeling that the water was going to come in. But it didn't. A trail of bubbles spread along the edge disturbing my vision, but that was all. An eddy twisted and contorted the image of George's face. I inhaled, and again the mask clung tight. I could feel the pouch on my chest swelling and going flat again as I breathed. I was under water and breathing, really *breathing*.

I emerged radiant. Then Claud fastened the straps over his own red hair. When he emerged he did not say a word, but just lovingly stroked the old hot-water bottle which had been mended with a couple of patches. Then, thoughfully, he asked if we hadn't found that the mask caused us to squint under water. This we indignantly denied.

To be truthful we did not breathe under water better than "on top of the Eiffel Tower", but nonetheless Donald was a wonderful piece of engineering, the key to our marvellous kingdom, our first apparatus that worked. It seemed to me to be worth all the apparatus that we made subsequently, to say nothing of those we had made before and which had never worked. George could no longer possess himself:

"Come on, let's go and show Donald to old Rebufat. He won't believe his eyes."

That at least we were well able to believe!

* * *

Nothing else mattered during the two days that lay between us and Sunday. I imagined a hundred things happening to hinder us and, though the barometer was at "set fair" I listened to all the weather forecasts fearing a sudden storm.

On Saturday evening I was unable to get to sleep. It was nearly midnight when the telephone in the hall rang. I went to answer it, as I always did, and lifted the receiver rather apprehensively, thinking it might be to call it off. It was George. He had not been able to get to sleep either. He asked if I was in form and all well.

"Yes, fine. And you?"

"Fine."

We had not anything more to say, yet neither wanted to hang up.

"Thank you, Francis," George said at last, "it would never have been possible without all of you. I've wanted to thank you for a long time. Now it's the real thing, serious, you realize that?"

"Yes, I know."

George was not one for sentiment, so I was all the more moved by that speech.

I went back to bed and read great chunks of *Twenty Thousand Leagues Under The Sea* to send me to sleep.

"We had at last arrived on the borders of this forest, doubtless one of the finest of Captain Nemo's domains. He looked upon it as his own, and considered he had the same right over it that the first men had in the first days of the world. And, indeed, who would have disputed with him the

74

possession of this submarine property? What other hardier pioneer would come, hatchet in hand, to cut down the dark copses?"

Like Professor Aronnax I was on the eve of my first submarine excursion. The algae, posidons and sea-fans of the cove would be an honourable baptism in place of the forests of the island of Crespo.

*　　*　　*

I found George and Philip already at the church. Claud was to be waiting for us when we came out.

The Scouts were there too, grouped in the chancel, and the chaplain was saying Mass. George was rather pale and intent on his missal. Then came the songs that we knew so well. Instinctively the words rose to my lips, but I wondered whether I ought to sing, because George was not. Philip was just moving his lips without uttering a sound, but he always did that because he had such an atrocious voice. I would have liked to have sung, especially on a morning like that, before my first dive. It is very difficult not to sing when everybody else is singing and you know the words. I thought that George would leave immediately after the Benediction so as to avoid a meeting outside, but no, he did not do anything of the kind. Evidently he had decided to let the Scouts go first.

George stayed on for a long time praying with his head in his hands, and the Scouts had long since left the church by the time we three got up. Outside, George was just tying the pump on to his bicycle when a fair-haired little scout we did not know came running back. On his shoulder he had the Elk badge of our old patrol and its fluttering flash. As he ran past he shot a glance at the buckles of our Scout belts, the only common article of our queer uniforms; then his eyes fell on the pump and Donald, but he said nothing and disappeared into the church.

Philip is one of those who always says what is in his mind and usually at the wrong moment.

"It's silly, but now I can't see a khaki shirt on top of navy blue trousers without a lump getting into my throat."

George kept his head bent over his luggage-carrier and pretended not to have heard.

*   *   *

George was in water up to his shoulders. For the third time he eased the edge of the mask so that he could breathe a little fresh air. His voice sounded indistinct:

"You must pump more quickly."

It was no good. Once again George laboriously heaved himself up on to the rock half suffocated.

"I'll try once more."

But no, the thing was bewitched. On dry land it worked perfectly, artificial lung well distended, mask flooded with fresh air, but the moment he got back into the water George would feel the hot-water bottle empty and flat, and the rubber snout would press like a gag over his face.

"It ought to work; it can't not work; it worked in the bath."

George stared at the mask as though it were an insoluble enigma. The inside was wet with the condensation from his breath. Was the Marvellous Kingdom to escape us after all.

"I've got it!" exclaimed Claud. "When we went on our backs in the bath, the mask and the lung were immersed at the same time and remained at the same pressure. Here

76

we are upright and the hot-water bottle goes in first. It collapses under the pressure and all the air escapes under the sides of the mask which, being higher, is subjected to a slighter pressure."

"What can we do?" groaned Philip.

George is not one to hesitate in such situations. He likes swift, decisive solutions:

"We must just go in head first."

"How?"

"We'll let a rope down with a boulder tied to the end and then we'll haul ourselves in with our arms, head first with our feet in the air."

That's what we did, and ever afterwards Donald worked perfectly. Thus I entered the Marvellous Kingdom head first, next after George and before Philip and Claud.

Slowly I went in. At first the water was foamy against the glass, almost impenetrable; then the miracle happened. The sea closed round me; the light became liquid and without shadow. The world of man had disappeared and my real life begun. At first I could see nothing but a deep blueness, a calm blue without blur or crack, only with here and there an arrow of deeper light like those that filter through the stained glass windows of a church or through the foliage of a forest interior, shafts of diffuse brightness, some slanting, some parallel, some even converging, like the spokes of a wheel, on some mysterious depth.

Slowly my groping hands pulled me along the rope. I did not dare turn round to see how far the surface was above me. The artificial lung on my chest was swelling and emptying in mechanical respiration, and the bubbles escaping in little mushrooms from my temples ran all along my slanting body as they rose. I was dazzled by it

all, and half-way between the surface and the bottom
halted to let myself gyrate slowly round the vertical rope,
like a weathercock on a lightning conductor. A shoal of
glittering fish with horizontal silver stripes were browsing
just below me, but then they took fright and fled in a
bunch, passing in front of the protruding eyepieces of
the mask and settled a little farther with their little
mouths still active.

That is the only distinct memory I have of that first
dive. I could not tell you exactly what I saw, because
everything demanded attention, and I had not yet acquired
that faculty that you only get after much practice, of being
able to disregard nine wonders to concentrate on observing
one.

Nor could I say how long I stayed under.

Fleeting pressure of the rubber snout on my face, a cold
trickle along my temples and I felt for the first time that
transient spasm which in the end we came to regard as an
essential part of a dive. For the first time I had to steal
away from the world of the depths which I had dared to
penetrate, and while my body hastened in pursuit of the
bubbles making for the security of the light, the splendours
I had glimpsed tugged at my heart and mind which were
laid under their spell for ever.

9

Now that at last we have caught up with our dream and can dive each day with this most efficient apparatus, we like to remember the difficulties of the early days and compare them with what is possible to-day.

I am writing these notes on paper that is spattered with salt water and grains of sand after having been on an enchanting visit to our ghost ship. I am left frustrated by the impossibility of finding the right words, for the right words just do not exist. George is happy with his camera. Thanks to steel and compressed air he is able to bring back to the light of men more than just a desperate longing. Even so he can only record visions bereft of the ineffable sensations that accompany them, complete them and bestow on them their supreme character of tangible unreality.

Claud too is happy with his chalks and his brushes. I still remember that June morning when he showed me his first pictures: blue, eight or ten different blues, graduated from pure deep blue to the turbid cadaverous blue-green of the divers' bodies: five pictures with the same treatment, without top or bottom, either with nothing to indicate direction, or else perforated by the guide-rope, a vertical not even in the plane of the picture, bereft of its importance in a world where weight no longer exists.

Before that we had suspected clever-fingered Claud of preferring the apparatus to the things it made possible, of being merely the poor technician who makes treasures without being able to profit by them. What a surprise his pictures had been!

I believe that, paradoxically, only a musician could fully express those ineffable dreams and that Realm of Great Silence. It calls for a new New World Symphony where a rustling of violins, slightly dissonant, would mark the slow departure from the surface which grows hazy and vanishes behind a sea-green "sky", while the diver continues to plunge into the heart of "a softly resonant haze"; then would come the dramatic crescendo of the revelation of the frothing wreck that suddenly appears beyond the haze, looms up, enormous, filling the entire eye-piece of the diver's mask, while the escaping bubbles of the diver ahead are strung out from bottom to top, barring the preternatural apparition with a delicate harp *arpeggio*.

All my companions have those images in their eyes.

I watched them this evening as we sat round the fire, George, Philip, Claud, Alan and I. The look in Philip's eye was avid and tense; Claud's observant and interested, George's triumphant, but Alan's eyes were misted and pathetic, as though the water were too great a burden. Yet they all had one thing in common, something indefinable which was at the same time the flame of adventure and the mist of dreams, dreams that we entered into each day, fearlessly and methodically. Thanks to this we were now a unit, a team, or, better still, able to be several teams capable of interchanging their members and yet always being homogenous, coherent and indivisible: in the slight haze of the medium depths, through the labyrinth of the wreck, or even in the blue twilight of twenty-seven fathoms right at the bottom of the submarine valley encased in its overhanging sides. We were a team indissolubly bound for life.

But it had not always been like that. I have just mentioned the name of Alan as being one of us. Fate is indeed ironical and plays strange tricks.

It was shortly after our first dives with Donald, when everything was easy to us and it wasn't so much a question of conquering a world as of consolidating our possession of it and making it more natural. George, tired of always diving with his head down, was trying a new apparatus, a helmet, which consisted of a large metal bell open at the bottom and resting on the shoulders of the diver, having a large port-hole in front and being fed by air by the traditional rubber tube that ended in the no less traditional pump.

That Sunday I was diving and I can see the scene as though it were yesterday. George put the bell over my head. The shoulder pieces bruising my skin; slowly I let myself go down following the rope which acted as a handrail, the two metal weights fastened to the helmet banging on my back and chest. Slowly the water rose up over my rectangular window, the light green inexorably driving back the blue of the sky. As always there was a pleasant little clutch at your heart as the blue vanished. The air made a noise like a gong being struck as it escaped by the shoulder pieces, and the metal helmet quivered. My pupils dilated. Then on the screen of my window began a wonderful film in slow motion: first, short, vertical algae which moved less and less, till they became stationary in modified light. Then, a little above me appeared a milky umbrella tinged with violet round the rim; slowly the jellyfish floated along the wall of rock, swimming though I could scarcely see how, and trailing its stinging tentacles beneath it. Perhaps it was born of a similar jellyfish or perhaps of polyp, an animal plant fixed to rock and which it in its turn would reproduce after a generation. It must have been aware of my presence, for the pulsations of its cap became more rapid and more powerful. Suddenly it heeled over, and in three lithe bounds it has gone from the blue screen of the window. To my companions up in the air I must have looked rather like an enormous jellyfish myself, disappearing and being absorbed into the depths.

Alone. An inch or so beneath my chin the water lapped against the inside of the helmet automatically putting the air in equilibrium, while, just above my head, the one-way valve thumped with the same rhythm as the pump up above on the surface. At that depth the excess of air escaped with a comical gurgling sound. The bubbles passed level with the glass, rising like insects in a hurry. The great helmet rolled and pitched like a sunken galleon on its way down to the bottom. Phrases from the tales of old Rebufat echoed in my ears (their drums felt hard): "The biggest is the devil-fish, but the octopus is the real lad . . . that time I fell from the keel of the wreck, my suit went flat, I was squashed, my head felt as though it was in a scuttle . . ."

It was at that moment that I felt a heaviness coming over me and my hands tightened slightly on the stiff rope. Then I let myself go again, but not too quickly so as to allow the pump time to counteract the increased pressure. Six feet above the bottom I let go of the rope and slid with the gestures of a sleep-walker to the golden sand of the bottom, where I landed among two bushes of sea-fans.

I felt like someone on the moon; I had no weight, no route, was walking across ground that was fluid, where the slight tracks I left were at once smoothed and effaced, vanishing beneath the pressure of twenty-five feet of water.

This was my eighth time down at that depth, which was no longer intimidating. The mystery had yielded to familiarity, and I felt rather as though I were the gardener of some magic garden where the plants are live animals that move and change position at the will of a redoubtable, but benevolent wizard. I collected a store of saffron-yellow sea-fans, which I knew would be salmon pink on the surface, then I went back to the rope and began to pull myself up towards the surface. My temples were hammering and I was breathing very quickly. The air supply was not good and I promised myself that I would mention it to George. Our little pump that was large enough to renew the air in the artificial lung was probably too weak to aerate that large metal bell which required forty-four pounds of weights front and back to submerge it. Laboriously, I hoisted myself out of the water.

George was not there to unhook the weights back and front and remove the dripping helmet. It was Claud who attended to me, getting me out of my submarine walker's equipment as well as he could alone. I was just going to ask him what had happened to the other two, when I saw them coming back down the terraced rocks, shoving a third figure in front of them. When they got closer I recognized the fair-haired little Scout who had passed us when he ran back into the church that Sunday five months before when we had made our first successful experiment. George and Philip had him tight, holding him with his arms twisted back and well up towards his shoulders, so that he walked along bent almost double, digging his feet in and staggering in the pools and over the rocks. One knee was bleeding, his hair was dishevelled and his khaki shirt was hanging in strips from his shoulders.

"Admit that you were spying on us," barked George. Then turning to me he said:

"I bet it's through this little fool that the Scout Master got to know about the Baby's Bottle."

"Why? What makes you think Maurice knows about the Baby's Bottle?" asked Claud.

George realized that he was on treacherous ground and did not reply.

"Admit that you were spying on us."

"We must find a nice torture for him: throw him to congers or give him to a muraena," suggested Claud.

Philip was less blood-thirsty, but his suggestions were considerably more practical and hence more terrifying:

"We could force him to eat a sea-slug raw, or put a baby octopus down the neck of his shirt."

The eyes of the young Scout misted over with tears and you could see from his face that he was afraid. He tried to wrest himself free, but it was no use. Philip twisted his arm up higher and made him cry out with the pain.

"Don't stampede, baby. Keep still."

All at once I saw on our prisoner's chest the two white strips of the patrol leader. The discovery called forth a fresh salvo of laughter.

"Shivering with fright? Fine thing for a patrol leader to do! What would the others say now if they could see you?"

The boy jerked beneath the lash of the insult, sniffed very loudly and turned his head aside in an effort to hide his tears.

Philip was growing impatient:

"Well, what shall we do?"

"One might even make him try the mask," I suggested.

George flung me a glance that was meant to be ferocious.

"No," he said, "we must know why and for whom he was spying on us with glasses from the top of the cliff and taking notes which he swallowed when he saw us. Was it the Scout Master who told you to do it?"

The only reply was an even louder sniff.

"All the worse for him if he won't talk! Let's take his shoes from him and that will give him a couple of miles across sharp rock before he gets back to the road."

We all applauded the idea. The Scout let us take his shoes without resistance.

"And don't come back here any more, and tell your Scout Master that we have nothing more to do with him, or he with us, and he shouldn't meddle in our affairs. Now, off with you."

We doubled up with laughter as we saw the unfortunate boy walk off with arms outstretched as he tiptoed among the sharp rocks. When he got to the little headland, he turned and shouted something. We thought it sounded like "See you again", but the wind carried the sound away and it was difficult to be sure. What happened next was done so quickly that we did not understand straight away. The next moment the boy, fully dressed, had disappeared into the water making a great fountain of spray.

"He's fallen in," cried Philip in a frightened voice, getting ready to dive in after him.

"No, he's making for the point. He jumped in."

George shaded his eyes with his hands and watched the swimmer whose head showed black against the sparkling water in the troughs of the waves.

"The little devil's going to swim back."

There was still a glare of irritation in George's eyes, but I thought I could also see a gleam of tenderness.

That was our first contact with Alan.

* * *

It was about this time that we made the acquaintance of old Professor Hornbostel. You may have read his *chef d'œuvre*, a masterly essay on the posterior salivary gland of the octopus. I have not, even though he presented us with a copy with a fine dedication.

George towed him out to the cove one day with his white hair, half-boots and immense umbrella, which we once used to catch jelly-fish without hurting them.

He did not know how to swim, let alone dive, and he plied us with endless questions about what we found, his eyes glowing with unquenchable curiosity. I can still see him armed with his enormous magnifying glass examining all that we brought him from the bottom of the sea: green or red starfish, sponges, sea-cucumbers, spirographes, polyps, ascidians, etc. After old Rebufat and George's father he was the first grown-up to take a real interest in our adventure, and we liked him for it and did all we could to satisfy him.

There was a certain *holothuria niger* which he especially wanted us to get him, and each time we dived wearing the helm with its plume of bubbles, we felt like knights in the service of an aged, benevolent king searching for a talisman that could never be found.

* * *

It was about this time that it was decided to install a telephone in the helmet. The idea was Claud's, who complained that he felt horribly lonely under the water, but no doubt it was really just an excuse for a bit of tinkering. George's parents, who followed our experiments with considerable interest, were also eager to see the telephone installed. I don't know why.

I was all against it. As it was, before each of our dives we had to endure George's interminable recommendations which were followed by demonstrations of the best way to breathe so as to economize air, how to walk to avoid upsetting the helmet, how to swallow your saliva so as to equalize the pressure on the middle ear using the Eustachian tubes, or how to spit on the glass of the window to prevent it misting, etc., etc. Thus I viewed with horror the approach of the time when George would be able to pursue us with his advice thirty feet below the surface.

The telephone was installed towards the end of July. It was pretty complicated and Claud had every justification for being proud when he showed us his handiwork. With the helmet on you had a pair of old headphones clasping your head like an instrument of torture. To the right of the window was an enormous microphone riveted between, "Don't leave this where children can get at it" and, "It is dangerous to lean your head out of the window." With this on my head I felt in danger of electrocution, but even so it did make you feel important and I stalked with added dignity among the rocks with their mossy coverings of algae and the bushes of seaweed.

The telephone worked for two Sundays and it was appalling, just as I had foreseen. The surface post had the code name "Caesar" in memory of our first association, and the helmet was "Cleopatra". I can't think why we needed code names when there were only the two stations, but George wanted to do everything according to the book, and he probably saw himself at a proper exchange giving orders to an army of divers.

The moment the waters closed over the top of the helmet those on land became most excited, crackling their solicitude in your ear so that you thought it would never end:

"Caesar calling Cleopatra, Caesar calling Cleopatra, how are you Cleopatra? Cleopatra, how are you? Don't forget to swallow your saliva, Cleopatra, and if you get too much pain in your ears, try to blow your nose in your fingers. . . . Do you hear me, Cleopatra? Answer, Cleopatra, answer . . ."

And you had to answer. Philip used to supply one or two forceful phrases which reassured George; then one day I decided to keep silent, but when I was six feet from the bottom the safety cord fastened to the top of the helmet suddenly went taut and I was hauled up at express speed.

George was quite pale and apologetic.

"I thought you had fainted." Then he added: "It will be the pressure that makes the membrane of the damned microphone stick."

That saved me from having to explain, but after that I always replied.

These love duets between Caesar and Cleopatra only lasted a short time. It was the microphone in the helmet that went first, so that Cleopatra heard Caesar, but Caesar no longer heard Cleopatra.

I was the diver on that occasion too. I had gone down a little lower than usual, to about thirty-five feet, on a preliminary sounding. Having abandoned the study of cephalopods Professor Hornbostel had asked us to bring him up green starfish and, of course, sea-slugs, always sea-slugs, as many sea-slugs as possible. We asked the Professor whether he followed the example of his colleague, Professor Aronnax of the *Nautilus*, and ate these juicy slugs between dolphin's liver and anemone jam. Somewhat surprised, the Professor replied that it was not for eating he wanted them; but that he required them for the study of some virus. In the hollow of the rocks I found one of an unusual species, being smaller than the average and apparently made of maroon velours. Perhaps this was *holothuria niger*, the elusive talisman? As soon as I picked it up, it shrunk together and then, furious, spat out wisps of ropy mucus that congealed at once in the cold water, enclosing my bare hand in a thin pale mauve net. A useless defence! I was not going to let it go for just that! Already I could see Professor Hornbostel's delighted face bent over his microscope.

It was at that moment that I felt the first symptoms of carbon-dioxide asphyxia. Despite the freshness of the helmet, the metal inside of which was running with the condensation of my breath, I felt the blood rushing to my head and my breathing growing quicker and quicker.

At once I stopped moving. For once, I thought, this dreadful telephone will serve some purpose.

"More air! Pump faster!"

Then idiotically I thought that perhaps George, being a stickler for form, would wait for me to announce my code name:

"This is Cleopatra. Caesar, pump faster."

I did not feel in the least like laughing. Through the earphones came the voice of Caesar, unperturbed:

"Hallo, Cleopatra, have you found any nasty sea-urchins? Don't prick your fingers, Cleopatra, be careful. And don't forget the Professor's sea-slugs."

"Pump quicker, for heaven's sake, pump *quicker*!"

"Cleopatra, the sea-urchins I mean are about the size of small melons and they should distinctly be of the symmetry of the fifth order."

That day it really was touch and go, and I don't know how with my confused sight and groping hands I managed to find the rope and haul myself up the few feet that saved the situation. After that we realized that it was no use counting on the telephone, and above all that with that heavy contraption on our heads twenty-five feet was quite a reasonable limit.

On the third Sunday the earphones suddenly gave up, abruptly and definitely. The salt water, the pressure, our absurd manipulations had got the better of them, so we went back to the good old system of Rebufat's life-line: one tug, all right; two tugs, more air; repeated tugs, danger. However, we did not dismantle the telephone for the time being, Claud pretending that the mere presence of the headphones and microphone acted as a sort of moral comfort. The truth was that it made the helmet look more like a piece of scientifically designed equipment. Later, when the reporters of the local papers started coming to see us, we had much better and more ingenious equipment to show them, but it was always that damned old helmet that interested them most.

Even now, when George shows visitors to our base, our ultra-modern equipment: high-pressure bottles of special alloy, pressure-reducers delivering air on demand, mouth-pieces that are the result of minute study, whole face goggles of safety glass, foam-rubber combinations to protect the diver from the cold, and beautifully stream-lined feet, the visitors just nod their heads gravely and squint across at the old helmet of riveted metal placed like a fetish in one corner of the room.

"And how does that one work?"

Eagerly they examine the old brute that nearly asphyxiated me and which still has its telephone in place between the jesting notices, and a dreamy look comes into their eyes.

Perhaps this is because that awful old box is so much more suggestive of the classic idea of divers with knives fighting horrible devil-fish, or of the mysterious Captain Nemo, ice-axe in hand, walking with Professor Aronnax along the abrupt slopes of the volcanoes of submerged Atlantis.

The more dreamy of the visitors ask:
"Do you ever use it for diving now?"
And George, who hates to kill their dreams, says:
"Oh, from time to time."

SOME time after that we began using masks with breathing tubes designed for submarine fishing, which George's father bought for us. Although these were not good enough for submarine exploration, for the true prince of the Marvellous Kingdom is not content to soar above it at a great height or to enjoy it for just the few seconds he can hold his breath, they were very convenient for keeping watch over the diver. Thus, above the knight of the deep with his weighted belt, helmet plumed with bubbles, one of us slid along the surface like a more lightly equipped squire. Thanks to the mask and its curved tube the squire was able, without stopping breathing, to keep watch on what lay beneath, the indistinct plain about which his lord and master over whose life it was his duty to guard, slowly moved, the bubbles from the reassuring plume coming up to swell and burst quite close to him or even caressingly against his sides and the glass window of his mask.

Thus, by seeing the others, we each of us got a picture of ourselves, of how we must look under thirty feet of water, and it was most impressive to see that figure, foreshortened by the refraction and blurred by the sea-green haze, crawling about the bottom like a big crushed crab. Never before had we thought thirty feet of water so deep.

It was not more than a fortnight after that that the parcel arrived.

That day I had walked back from school with George as usual. True to tradition he was getting ready to walk back with me to my home (one day we had seen each other home six times!) when his mother called to him:

"George, there's a parcel for you and your friends."

"Who from?"

"A young girl put it down by the garden gate. I came out when I saw her, but she had gone already. I didn't know her."

It all sounded very mysterious.

The parcel was addressed to all four of us. George broke the string. First there was a lot of brown paper, then some corrugated cardboard, and finally a long, rectangular box.

We were struck dumb by what we saw: long ribbed rubber frogmen's feet, four pairs of flippers. We took them out with as much care as though they had been made of glass. George tested the spring of the ribs, caressed the long shape of them; we looked at each other ecstatically.

"Oh," said George, "who's done this?"

At first we thought it must be George's parents, but they protested so vehemently that we had to believe them. And George told me that his parents never lied to him. Nor could they have any reason for doing so in this case.

That very evening Philip and Claud came to take possession of their flippers.

The mystery remained.

* * *

As we practised twice a week, we soon became pretty good with our new equipment, but also dissatisfied with only using it to watch over the diver from the surface. We began, therefore, to practise free diving, at any rate on the days that we did not take the helmet with us. Apart from the fact that it was excellent exercise, it enabled

Philip and Claud to hunt; harpoon fishing being allowed in France only on condition that you do not use breathing equipment. Philip had once tried to take a spring-gun manufactured by Claud down with him when diving with the mask, but George had made a fearful fuss and that had been the end of it.

For free diving we abandoned the cove that we knew too well and went to other parts of the coast. One favourite spot was where there was a slow descent down the red friable rock, to where an abandoned blockhouse, girdled with barbed wire, still threatened the sea with its armoured embrasures. Danger, mines. Danger, unexploded ammunition. War and death; blood and destruction. Then the welcoming water, light green, frothy shingle, two pillars once graced with chains, girt with submarine *chevaux-de-frise* intended to smash the hulls of landing boats.

We hurried to get out to where it was deepest, to the sea-green peace where a flock of saupes might be grazing. Bodies gathering, then slackening; legs vertical above the water, then a long glide without jar or noise, straight as an arrow. At the exact moment when the water closes over them, our flippers begin to thresh with great powerful strokes. George, ballasted with lead, plunged down in a steep dive. We had to follow down the slope slipping upwards, marbled red with algae among the sea-urchins and anemones, and then at twenty-five feet the more distinct line of the grey sea-fans.

Suddenly the mask went flat on my face and I exhaled slightly through my nose to release it. My cheeks went hollow, became moulded round the big mouthpiece that I held clenched between teeth and gums. With regular big scissor movements of his flippered feet George was still going down and down at the head of his patrol. My ear-drums went hard, seemed to stick. You needed to swallow. Claud gave up and rose like an arrow; then Philip too. Like a flash I saw their flippered feet pass my window on the way up towards the air and the light. I was proud of being able to follow George a little farther down, to forty feet. Bracing one hand against the mossy rock he wrested off a big sea-fan, then with one thrust of his flippers moved away from the overhang and rose up vertically, arms by his sides, the gleaming glass of his mask's window turned towards the light, while all along its rubber edge mushrooms of bubbles took form and expanded, that being the air he had exhaled into the mask on the way down to keep it from going flat against his face. Facing each other we shot up in dizzy ascent. What a long time it took. George smiled. Then came foam, the surface and the sunlight.

Philip had fired his cross-bow near the mouth of a cave some twenty-five feet down. Under water the click was audible for a long way. Now he was back on the surface, reeling in on his nylon line some prey that we could not yet see. It was putting up a fight. A black mass emerged out of the haze. No, it was no good; he had to give it some line, go down again. Philip handed the gun to Claud, gathered himself, then dived. In a moment he emerged again holding in both hands his dart and on it in its death throes the *mérou* he had shot point-blank, a game fish reputed to be "royal", a fine fish, thick-lipped and good-natured.

So much for the peace of the deep!

Claud helped Philip to tow in the dying fish. Gliding along the surface George and I watched its execution, fascinated though scornful. When hauled up on the shingle the squat fish proved to be more than three feet long.

"Are you proud of yourselves?" asked George.

"I should say so!" Philip replied.

George looked at the blockhouse, the barbed wire, then at the dead fish with an arrow through its gills.

"I wonder", he said quietly, "just how deep you have to go."

Before making his first dive a pupil receives final directions

Working the hand-pump to supply air to the diver

11

I HAVE just read through what I wrote yesterday. Philip has now turned over a new leaf and scarcely hunts at all. At least he never hunts just for the sake of hunting, but only to add to our provisions when that becomes necessary. Also he only harpoons the larger fish and confines his activities to one side of the island, in which sector we have resigned ourselves to having to play the part of the dangerous shark. Thus our one and only underwater gun is scarcely ever used. But surely to make friends with a little octopus, no longer to frighten the big *mérou* of the wreck, and to be able to come up slowly without scaring it, are victories more difficult to achieve and more valuable than the extermination of *sars* or mullet.

But, perhaps you will say, don't fish eat each other? Yes, of course, as all wild creatures do, but only for food. So that's what we do.

Under water, as in Mowgli's kingdom, man is the only one to infringe the sacred law of the jungle. He kills for the sport of it, as a game. After our first few dives with the helmet, when we had collected a certain number of specimens for Professor Hornbostel, the grown-ups deigned to admit that we were not altogether mad and almost the first questions they asked were "What especially do you hunt?" and "Do you catch many?" for they could not believe that one could dive without hunting or watch without trying to kill.

It was partly due to Philip's father casually announcing in the office: "Yesterday my son went down to forty feet in their diving helmet" and partly to George's mother dragging her friends to see the pink sea-fans in her china cabinet in the drawing-room, that we began to become known. The news of our dives spread with the inevitable result that we became easy game for our local reporters in search of "copy".

The Communists were the first on the scene. Philip wanted to refuse them an interview, but George would not hear of it. The Marvellous Kingdom admitted of no politics. Truly Machiavellian, George murmured vaguely about necessary publicity and possibility of future subsidies, but I believe he would have let himself be interviewed by Satan on the subject of our dives. Not that there was anything satanic about the Communist reporter. He was a fat placid creature, the sort of person who would die of fear if he had to put his head under water, but who will ask you point blank how it is that you have not yet been down to thirty fathoms.

Having replied resignedly to the usual, "What do you hunt?" "Have you caught many?" George showed the man everything and explained everything:

"Below twenty feet there's no more red, none at all. Red as a colour disappears."

"Well, that's very interesting, most interesting", muttered our Communist, his pencil galloping about his little black note-book.

We received plenty of others after him, and that is what made George develop his little eccentricity: his way of expressing esteem is to invite you to undress on the spot and accompany him into the depths. I even suspect that the depth to which he takes you is proportional to the extent of his regard. If you have the misfortune to be "noticed" by George, then at the first opportunity you will be for 130 feet!

At that time, of course, we were not going as deep as that, but the interviews accorded in the drawing-room of George's house quickly evolved into proper demonstrations in the little cove. George would dive in the helmet, undo the straps, drop to sixteen feet and take a semi-respiration to avoid any risk of bursting his lungs, and then emerge without the helmet, his fair hair flat and streaming, rather like a nice porpoise. Then Philip, displaying his great feet like a spider-crab, would tip in a duck dive and going down sixteen or eighteen feet insert his head into the empty helmet, like a hermit crab taking up a new abode.

It was rather a spectacular little turn, and so too was the sequel. The unfortunate journalist, unaware of the fate in store for him, and loaded with new "copy", would start taking delighted leave-takings, when George would propose point-blank that he should try out the equipment for himself. Usually the unfortunate creature would blench and take a few steps away from the water's edge, and reply that to his "great regret" he could not swim.

It is incredible how many journalists cannot swim. We noticed that the proportion of non-swimmers in that profession was much greater than in any other!

Such a reply however would not defeat George. He would drag up to his victim's feet our enormous helmet.

"That doesn't matter at all", he would say in an authoritative tone, "this equipment is so heavy that you cannot swim with it. It's quite enough to walk—a little heavily—on the bottom."

He would ponder for a moment, then add as though it had suddenly occurred to him:

"In fact it's a good thing that you don't know how to swim, for then you might be tempted to let yourself go horizontal, and then . . ."

"What?" the journalist would ask.

"Then the helmet would overturn and fill with water, and you would be caught and held head down."

Only one reporter risked it, a timid little chap who called George, "Sir", and referred to us as "you divers". The helmet disappeared in a patch of foam, much to George's satisfaction, but I felt that we should never see him again, at least alive.

George put on an ordinary mask and went in with him, circling round the patch of bubbles and diving every now and again, legs together, flippers motionless till they were covered. As he came up from his third or fourth dive, he spat out his mouthpiece and shouted:

"I believe he's had it. He's not moving. He may have fainted. Get him up quick!"

Hauling as hard as we could, we extracted the journalist not from his faint but from ecstatic contemplation of wonders that had transfixed him, and he was quite indignant when he asked why on earth we had pulled him out so quickly.

After that he was a changed man. There was no more "sir"-ing; he slapped us on the back and told us what he thought would be the best way of walking so as not to tilt the helmet. Before he left he asked if he might come back the following Sunday and dive again:

"You see, I could write a whole series of articles?"

"But of course, with pleasure," said George, delightedly.

After the demonstration George usually concluded with a little jocular lecture on the main dangers at great depths: nitrogen narcosis or gaseous embolism.

Three or four days later the article would appear, usually under some quite sensational heading, such as: "At the frontiers of death", "Death and intoxication in the deep", or, the one we liked best, "Children among the devil-fish".

Reading those articles you would have thought that we were a band of young heroic madmen, drunk with oxygen, intoxicating themselves with nitrogen under pressure as others do with opium, and coming up again, always by sheer luck, from dives that normally ought to have cost them their lives. In fact, if George had not kept telling us that it was all sheer nonsense, we might have been impressed or even horrified.

*   *   *

And of course death was there, as in any other adventure, and we often thought of it. We always had done so, right from the beginning, especially George. I can remember him reading *Twenty Thousand Leagues Under The Sea* and going back again and again to the fascinating description of the submarine cemetery. I used to see him looking out dreamily at the immensity of the sea, and once he said to me, half-seriously:

"If I should die, I should like to be committed to the waters in a last dive, untrammelled and without a coffin, like a trappist or a corsair."

Yes, we thought of death quite often and more seriously than one might have been led to believe by our schoolboy pranks on journalists who were poor swimmers, not that there was anything spiteful or nasty about them, for, though not necessarily swimming "among devil-fish" or "roaming the frontiers of death", we were too aware of running definite risks and too often felt fear ourselves, for us to laugh at others on that score.

The fear we felt was a queer, purely intellectual fear that was almost always disassociated from any physical dread. I thought about it the day before yesterday when I was diving in our closed-circuit Pirelli apparatus. The sharp, warm air purified through soda lime rasping my throat made me remember that there were such things as "Shallow-water black-out" and "Blowing out" which, though they may sound more like a cocktail or a South American dance, can prove fatal. If the body does not shrink from the idea of a fracture, hæmorrhage, or burn, how could it falter at the thought of a conveniently brutal faint or pleasantly insidious narcosis? For us death was prepared to discard her fancifulness, and there were none of the monsters that Hans Andersen makes guard the palace of the Sorceress of the Sea round the inner temple that we sought beneath the waters. Once over the initial fears, a person mentally aware of the danger, can venture to the utter limit without the body shrinking and holding him back.

* * *

I shall long remember the November Sunday when I decided that I was going to do free diving by myself and pay a visit to the wreck of *Tozur*, a cargo vessel that was driven out to sea in 1936 and went aground on the island of Ratonneau. There being no public transport to the island itself I went on the ferry to the Château d'If and there, at the foot of the fort, I undressed, hid my clothes in a hollow in the rocks, and then putting on my mask and frogmen's feet and feeling rather brave I set course for the ruined houses of the island of Ratonneau. I arrived pretty fagged by a strong current, and on the other side of the island I found the wreck, though with a little difficulty. The fore-part was a devastated ruin, but the after-part still looked like a ship, heeled over on its side, pointing two pairs of derricks towards the surface and presenting to the pale light plates that were rusted and encrusted, and in which port-holes and scuttles gaped like traps. Five times I went down and caressed its thickened bulwarks. Then, hopping on the sharp pebbles, I recrossed the island to take to the water again on the Château d'If side.

Meanwhile the sea had become rough, and the waves were rolling across the channel. As I stood there shivering among rocks streaming with spray, the Château d'If with its girdle of breakers looked very far away. However, there was nothing else for it: there, on the other side, lay my warm clothes and my return ticket for the Marseilles ferry. I shall not forget that swim in a hurry! Every time I raised my head to look at the headland the waves shook my breathing tube as though trying to pull it off, and thumped on my old mask that was beginning to "go" at the edges and was already half full of water. It was November and the water was cold. I got cramp in the calf of my right leg, and then I reached that stage of exaggerated lucidity when you are aware of the slightest details: the trickle under the mask at your left temple, the water gathering at the bottom of the breathing tube which you no longer have the strength to get rid of; the current and the château which gets no nearer; then you get an insipid taste in your mouth and slowly the conviction grows that it is all to no purpose.

At last I did reach the shallows which were invisible under the troubled waters, but sizzling with the noise of the pharyngeal teeth of all the wrasse busy searching for their prey;[1] then I got to the sharp, corroded rocks and waited for a wave to come, which lifted me and deposited me like a stranded fish on the shingle. I covered the next few

[1] According to another theory this characteristic sound is caused by innumerable little shrimps each incessantly smacking together the two parts of the organ that they use to capture their prey.

yards on my knees, hampered by the frogmen's feet, till I reached the dry slope at the foot of the castle and found the hole where I had put my clothes.

After that struggle naked in the water, the rough thick wool of my sweater and sailor's trousers soon gave me a warm sense of security. Slowly my heart stopped pounding. In my place George would have laughed triumphantly, but I just thanked God and smiled a little at the joy that flooded me along with the warmth.

How sweet life was all of a sudden, and how lovely the sky. Perhaps after all those things have a value of their own; but in that case you must voluntarily risk losing them for that value to become perceptible. Or, rather, the details have no value of their own, only the glory lent them by our hearts and minds when in a state of what you might call spiritual security in temporal insecurity, with its dangerous wonderful joy that George personifies so well and without which we will now not be able to live.

*   *   *

We met each Saturday evening at George's home, gatherings that went on until late. In that atmosphere we seemed to be curiously receptive to shades of meaning, able to catch thoughts that were scarcely expressed.

On one such evening George switched off the lights and let the moonlight flood the big drawing-room so that the pink sea-fans again had their original yellow submarine pallor. George began reciting from memory, speaking softly, an ironic little smile on his lips as though to excuse himself and refute any appearance of pedantry:

> *Beneath the sea, like some mysterious aurora,*
> *The sun lights the forest of Abessynian coral;*
> *There in the depths of pools, warm and littoral,*
> *Creatures in flower mingled with live flora.*

The noisy enthusiasm of our early reunions in the nautical tarry odour of old Rebufat's house had now given place to a more subtle appreciation of our Adventure, and that old diver's tales of 300 cases of brandy in the sunken *Melpomène* had been replaced by the sonnets of José-Maria de Hérédia.

By a strange phenomenon of compensation George, now an athletic youth of seventeen, let himself be carried away on the thread of his one and only dream.

"And that, I say, is darned good. What do you think of it, Matto Grosso?"

Pour us your poison wine that makes us feel like gods!
Our brains are burning up!—there's nothing left to do
But plunge into the void!—hell? heaven?—what's the odds?

"Who's that by?"

"Baudelaire. 'We're bound for the Unknown'. See? On the eve of decisive conquests it is always the poets who lead the way; the technicians just march along behind to organize. And do you know these two lines from Jules Laforgue:

"Off and away, into the fleeting pasture you fled from me,
Or sent me invitation from the sky of the waters.

"But music is so much better than all that! Now that I know the submarine world, I feel when listening to some modern music that I now hold the key to its secrets."

In the moonlight George looked fairer than ever, and his face wore that frank, serious expression he puts on when he speaks of things that he has at heart. There was no sign now of his little exculpatory smile.

"Those sounds that used to mean nothing to me, have now become a source of vague impressions . . . landscapes never achieved by the methodical hand of man, landscapes without rule or symmetry, superbly independent and virgin, such as are only to be found in the Marvellous Kingdom.

"Francis, to-morrow you may have an extra dive, only go to the piano and play"—there was a note almost of supplication in George's voice—"you know, the piece you played a week ago."

I did as I was asked. How I love the cool give of the keys beneath my fingers.

12

THE floor of our cove is a sort of submarine plateau from twenty or thirty feet deep; it is shaped like a half-moon and in the centre is a little dip where there is perhaps forty feet of water. It was in that dip that I almost drowned the day that the microphone in the helmet failed.

Towards the open sea, at the limits of the cove on the straight side of the half-moon, the plateau drops away abruptly in a sheer slope, in fact there may even be a bit of an overhang. Here a slender upright rock protrudes almost up to the surface; it marks the symbolic frontier of our domain and we call it the frontier rock.

On several occasions I ventured at the end of the tube as far as this frontier rock and sat there with my two feet dangling over the abyss. I would hold on to a tuft of seaweed with one hand and with the other press on the base of the helmet so as to tilt it slightly forwards as I leaned over the chasm. Intestinal rumblings would shake the helmet as the mushrooms of air escaped by the shoulder pieces. In front, the water rose slightly to tickle my chin and lick at the bottom of the glass which was inclined towards the forbidden depths that were of the same calm blue, yet somehow more compact and more limpid, more perfect and even more mysterious than the light blue of my first dive. For some seconds my gaze would search that magnificent blue, where now and again a gleam of silver would appear and vanish again at once.

I would have liked the Scouts, the Chaplain, even the Scout Master, to have been able to feast their incredulous eyes on that. I wished that Alan, the fair-haired little Scout, could have seen me through his glasses, not on the surface, but as I was then balancing above the abyss in our enormous helmet on which George had painted a little T-shaped cross the colour of blood.

I imagined myself with a new and more perfect apparatus strapped on, gliding all alone down the curtain of immaculate water covering the vertical slope, emitting at intervals puffs of bubbles as I penetrated farther and farther downward towards the heart of the Marvellous Kingdom.

I dreamed of other equipment, armour loaded with air-cylinders, bathyscaphes . . . of going farther and farther, deeper and deeper, down to the motionless icy layers which are only plumbed by the bodies of drowned sailors in their unending descent, down to deeps to which no living being had yet penetrated, away beyond the mono-chrome detritus to the total obscurity of the immense plains of clay where the bones of the whales slowly become covered by the drift of sediment.

What a dream! My hands would clench, my head begin to swim from staring at that great blue emptiness full of shadows and sudden gleams. I would lean forward a little farther, just far enough to feel afraid, recoil with a sudden tug on the seaweed and move away from the precipice with a leap like that of a frightened devil-fish.

On such occasions when I had got back and removed the helmet it would be enough for George to take a look at me for him to say:

"You've been there again."

I would not even answer, but he was never wrong. I could tell by his tight smile that he felt the same confused attraction for that watery chasm. One day, just before diving, he said to me:

"Come to the house this evening and I'll show you something."

The words were almost the same as the ones he had used that time four years before, and suddenly I saw him again by that same cove in his sailor suit, holding a large sea-urchin in his hand. He had not changed. He had perhaps grown a little and his hair become a shade fairer, but he still had the same extraordinarily confiding, childish, waif-like expression, which returned to his face each time just before he put on the helmet or put the mouthpiece between his teeth.

"Come and see me this evening at nine o'clock", he repeated. Then the helmet engulfed him and I slipped into the water to keep an eye on him from above. That day he too went as far as our frontier. The sea was not very good, and in my mask and frogmen's feet I pitched in the channel just above him. When it was nearly at the surface, the column of his bubbles began to sway from side to side, breaking and balancing in time with the rhythm of the waves; but down where the pale silver column originated I could make out a pallor that was George, on the edge of the abyss, at the exact limit of the dark green of the plateau and the deep blue of the great emptiness where there were neither waves nor storms.

*   *   *

George's room was unchanged. There was the same Moroccan cover on his divan, the same lampshade with painted caravels and the heavy table like a work-bench. On the mantelpiece were George's favourite books, the works of his three heroes: Saint-Exupery, Larigaudie and T. E. Lawrence, books which George had taught me to love.

"Come and look at this."

109

George switched off the ceiling light. Under the concentrated light of his reading lamp he spread out some plans, his plans. After that nothing existed for us, but that circle of light and the diagrams.

"Three pumps like ours, a buffer bottle to regulate the flow, a gauge to show the inside pressure of the bottle, that is to say the diver's depth; sixty yards of nylon tube reinforced towards the surface; then the apparatus itself, a respiratory bag into which the feed-pipe leads, with a sunk mount inside and ending in a duck-bill valve with a flat socket to act as a non-return valve. A flexible collar tube leading from the bag to the mouthpiece and returning to the level of the bag where it ends in a really big exhaust valve which will avoid excessive dilation of the bag when returning to the surface. Underwater hunter's goggles, a weighted belt, frogmen's feet. . . ."

"How deep?" I asked with a delicious shiver.

George gestured vaguely:

"At least sixty feet; more perhaps. In any case it will give complete liberty of movement within the radius of the sixty yards of tube. There'll be no more need of a rope for going down and up, no more walking on the bottom, we'll swim between layers of water just as if we had independent apparatus; that is why I have allowed for frogmen's feet. In a way it's Donald back again, only with a mouthpiece, a good non-return valve, more air in a continuous supply. The old helmet can be relegated to the museum."

"And the money for it?"

"It won't be so dear. Cost less than the helmet. Claud will make us this easily. And my father has promised to help."

At that moment we were both sitting side by side on the table, legs dangling. The same thought came to us and we looked at each other, the same joyful light in our eyes, yet we never said a word. Suddenly George exclaimed:

"Why does it make us happy? A few feet more or less . . ."

Silence again, then George took a book from the mantelpiece: "Did you know that Larigaudie was an experienced diver? In *Echoes of the South* I have found some submarine descriptions that are among the best there are, particularly those of coral bottoms. One day he even weighted himself with lead, put on a pair of primitive goggles and went down with the pearl fishers. Listen to this:

"As I hung motionless in the midst of this marvellously warm, transparent water, I saw the bronze silhouette of the diver, with his white glove and large flowered pareo withdrawing into a rainbow of unreal colours, then becoming lost in a sort of blue night, while a little bubble of air slowly rose close beside the rope that was a yellow line joining the bottom and the surface."

"That reminds me of the old Rebufat's story of Yawl and the Pharaoh's treasure, do you remember, George?"

"Yes, I remember."

George sat thinking, one finger on a temple bathed in the soft light of the lampshade with its painted caravels. Never before had I been so strongly aware that his was one of those hearts that can shed their casing and rise superior to the body, overcoming its fear. I was fascinated and unable to take my eyes off his face with its desperately eager eyes and the livid little scar so apparent to me on the cheek.

Again his lips moved hesitantly, groping for the words to express a fugitive truth.

"There are times when I wonder. You see, Francis, we

think ourselves lords because we hold our lives cheap. At our age there's not much to that. But is it enough? One had to live, to construct. That's what I tell myself sometimes, don't you? You see, Francis, we're not fourteen any longer. It's no longer just a question of chosing between old Rebufat's models and Maurice's herbarium. Take the buildings at the harbour; even their reflections in the water are ugly. Or the dockers; there isn't a gleam in their eyes even when they look at the sea. Well, it's simple, isn't it? We just leave the harbour. And for us the sea is always beautiful. It's easy."

"Just now you quoted Larigaudie. He went off!"

"That was before the war, Francis. Would he go now? Have we the right always to go off?"

Silence.

"The question of period doesn't enter into it," I said quietly. "It's a question of principle. We are just like him and have the right to everything provided that we don't cheat and that we deliberately accept the risks. You mentioned Larigaudie. Do you remember the episode of his voluntary bathe among the sharks in *Echoes of the South*? One has the right to buy anything in exchange for one's own life."

George gave a sudden snort, stood up and walked to the window. The slightly crazy light had lit up again in his eyes and was dancing there at the back of them, and there was that slight, rather cunning smile at the corner of his mouth. Once more he was the rather too adventurous one who jumped the harbour gate and led a revolt against the Scout Master. His voice was again clear and mordant, and it had a ring that held promise of yet more delights and dangers.

"You are right. Besides, wasn't it Larigaudie who wrote: 'The world in which we live is not to our measure and sometimes our hearts are big with all our longing for Heaven.'

"Our Marvellous Kingdom is itself a good bit more to our measure, like an instalment of heaven."

13

ST. GEORGE'S EVE three years ago deserves mention for more than one reason. First it was George's birthday, but it was also the eve of the trials of our new apparatus. These were to start very early in the morning, so we had decided that we would all sleep at the cove, where old Rebufat, who this time believed in the apparatus, was to join us at dawn to attend to the boat during the trials, a job he would have yielded to none. The rest of us were already gathered round a camp fire on the rocks: Philip, tanned, a red handkerchief tied round his head making him look like a young South Seas pirate (he only lacked the earrings): Claud, touzled and unrecognizable, his freckles for once invisible beneath the red glow of the fire, and George, his hair now cropped except at the front, where a fair wisp quivered in the sea breeze like a plume.

Lower down there was the sea and the boat moored at the head of the cove and in it the large packing case with our equipment: the new apparatus which George had baptized "Kamikaze"—which means "divine wind"—the pumps, gauge, buffer bottle, masks, frogmen's feet, respirators, and also 130 feet of rope that was to be moored vertically with little numbered tags every fifteen feet which George would pluck as he made his slow descent in the morning and which would be irrefutable evidence of the depth attained.

Some green wood on the fire spluttered, and Philip unfolded his long legs.

"Do you remember four years ago?"

Four years before we had not yet left the Troop. There had been a camp fire inland with a sing-song and games.

"And afterwards Francis took his promise."

Yes, I had, but I was surprised that Philip should have remembered that.

"It was a good evening. Do you remember the Ayak Game?"

The topic was not to George's liking, I could see that, but I did not feel that I had the right to change the subject by suddenly talking of something else, so I kept silent too. That had been the last meeting before the break.... George had no regrets, and none of us on that anniversary regretted having followed George. No regret and no remorse either; after all the promise I had given then had been that I would act and behave as a man, not that I would follow Scout Master Maurice along paths that no longer interested me. My paths were those of George, the conquest of the sea.

At the most there was a slight taste of bitterness at having had to embark upon that alone, without Alan, without the chaplain, or any of the others. How grand it would have been on such an evening to have listened to the chaplain telling us of the sea, of discovery in its silent jungles, of its strange creatures, of the incredible phantasmagoria of the masterpieces of God's making in the dawn of creation. It would have been good, too, to have heard him speaking about the risk, comradeship, responsibilities, sacrifices, all the things that are so splendidly real and live beneath the hazardous sea and not just faked as when they are staged by an ingenious Scout Master for the sake of the cause on the land that has been conquered so long already, cut up and divided, fenced, organized, inhabited and trodden by man in his flocks.

The wind was rising, and Claud, who was in charge of the boat, got up and went to look at the moorings. I was busy with the fire when a light step made some twigs snap. Thinking it was Claud come back, I said "You've been quick," and never even raised my head.

But it wasn't Claud. It was a Scout, our fair-haired little Scout, Alan.

On the other side of the fire George leaped to his feet with a sudden movement as though to receive an enemy or an important visitor. They looked at each other across the fire, the one tensed and ready for all eventualities, the other assured, legs wide apart. The silence lasted several seconds. It was Alan who broke it.

"Here", he said and held out the patrol flag. I recognized the Elk emblem, emblem of our old patrol and the one we had seen on his shoulder at our first encounter outside the church.

George paled and involuntarily his muscles tensed. His voice was quite expressionless as he asked:

"Why this?"

We did not dare understand.

"To-morrow, when you go down you must fix it to your belt and afterwards you will keep it, if you wish", the voice hesitated, "and take over the patrol again to lead us where you like."

"But, I couldn't. And the Scout Master?"

"He agrees to try it out with you, accepts your ideas and anyone can go with you who wishes."

"Isn't he afraid?"

"Of course, he is. But he accepts all the same."

George pondered this, eyes on the ground and on his face that childish expression that he always has before diving or taking an important decision; then he smiled and looked Alan in the eye:

"With you as Second, I will."

The flag changed hands across the fire. Alan turned and made a gesture that conjured Scouts out of the shadows.

"There there are. I told them to hide and wait, because I didn't know if you would want to have their shoes off."

George flushed.

"By Jove", exclaimed George admiringly, "they're all ready with masks and frogmen's feet."

Alan walked round the fire, put his hand on George's shoulder.

"Of course, the same as those we sent you."

*   *   *

Together it made a big patrol of eleven and old Rebufat's boat was not large enough. Alan, however, had foreseen everything, except the possibility of George's refusing.

A sounding taken at the foot of the plateau had shown eighty-one feet and George had smilingly pronounced that enough for the first day. As he was fixing the descent rope George removed the patrol flag from his belt and tied it to the end of the rope near the iron weight that did duty as an anchor.

"Do you think you'll get right to the bottom?" Alan asked anxiously.

"Quite sure."

"And then you will bring the flag up again?"

"I will."

The weight went overboard. The rope slid swiftly through Alan's hands and every fifteen feet appeared a little numbered tag. When the fifth appeared the rope was still going out.

"George, it's more than seventy-five feet already."

"Let it run."

One foot from the second tag after that the rope stopped. The previous sounding must have struck a rock, or else the weight had this time struck a submarine valley or dip of some kind.

"One hundred and four feet!"

In justice to George it must be said that his hesitation was all but imperceptible.

"O.K. Fasten her to the bows. Prepare to dive. Put the apparatus on me. Philip: what we agreed, one pump from nil to fifteen feet, two pumps from there to fifty feet, and below that three. Connect up. Francis, you'll be escort."

My heart leaped with joy. I knew I wouldn't be going with him down to one hundred feet; I might hardly be able to follow him with my eyes, for silhouettes are quickly absorbed by the haze of the depths; but I would keep watch on the column of ascending bubbles which alone would show that George, invisible and far below, was breathing and alive. George had entrusted his life to me.

I can remember it all. The kamikaze was swelling on George's chest; then slowly, hampered by his big frogmen's feet, he heaved himself overboard. For some seconds he hung on his two hands, his body arched under the boat and surrounded by the bubbles of the exhaust valve that was already under water. Then his fingers opened.

At that moment the rather tremulous voice of old Rebufat sounded:

"And remember, lad, if the air stops coming, or anything goes wrong, you come up."

It was too late. George's head was already submerged and he heard nothing. A hand moved along the side towards the bows; then the thumb was stuck up. All was well. Then the hand vanished as well.

It was now my turn. I inserted the mouthpiece of the short breathing tube and slid from the boat. As I put my head in, I left the world of men. There was George. The water was already a magical translucent wall above him. For some seconds his motions were groping, as though he were both enchanted and embarrassed by the lightness of his body. His arms seemed to be searching the water. Then he found himself in the receptive water; his flippered legs caught the rhythm, he dipped and began to slide down towards the bottom. Now his hand had encountered the rope that stood rigid like a sword; slowly and alone, he went down and down towards the blue depths.

The bubbles that came from the exhaust valve were not round, but rather like jellyfish, and as they came slowly up they swelled and swung from side to side till they suddenly exploded in a sputter of light. George must have turned and seen my silhouette black against the light, for I saw him gesture. Gradually he disappeared. For a while I caught occasional glimpses of a gleaming green flipper or of his fair hair waving like a pale sea anemone. Then there was nothing.

No doubt, if George had looked up he would not have seen either me or the sky, not even the boat like a captive balloon at the end of its rope. Now he would be down at eighty feet, and blood would be trickling from his left nostril; that was always his weak one. It would be trickling down his face and very gradually filling the bottom of the mask. There was nothing of him to be seen, nothing but the silver column of bubbles, wavering and ascending, shifting and moving round the rope, its source lost in the haze.

Although I could not see George, I knew that he was gliding among the ghastly sea-fans of a frozen landscape; that his chest would be brushing fields of weed powdered with white, that he would be groping among slimy rocks and algae. Then he would go lower still to the bottom of the submarine valley beneath the press of its waters, where he must recover a flag. Black fish would dart away at his approach and settle again inquisitively a short distance off.

Bubbles, bubbles. George was alive and breathing.

George was coming up, a pale blur like a phantom. Then the outlines became more distinct, I could see his legs with the big frogmen's feet retracting and striking out. Then he raised his head as though to judge the distance he had still to go before he got to the surface, and a shaft of light flashed on the glass of his goggles. Attached to George's back was something that fluttered like the pale wing of a bird. So he had got down to the bottom. Now he was quite close, but coming up slowly to give his blood time to become purified of its excessive nitrogen. Twelve feet—six feet.

How I admired George, lying in the water alongside the rope, helping himself along with a slight movement of his flippers, so lithe and supple. Up he came and broke the surface quite close to me.

*   *   *

With the weighted belt it was difficult for George to climb back into the boat, so in the end we hoisted him in like a tunny in its net, on to the floor-boards. And then we cheered. We cheered George, we cheered the Underwater Scouts, we cheered the Marvellous Kingdom.

While George took off the apparatus we produced our thermos flasks and a bottle of cognac. George's eyes were alight with the glow of a dual triumph. A few drops of blood dropped from the mask on to the flag that was sodden and heavy with sea water; our flag.

14

I HAVE not written anything for ten days. It is queer how action and work, especially literary work, are so essentially different, almost opposites. Perhaps the need to write, the urge to transmit, is merely a counter-irritant, the need for which disappears as soon as we are offered the satisfaction of risking and achieving. And to think that there are people who are content just to write. What a shameful vice!

I sometimes wonder what is the point of going on writing. As the Master of Santiago said, "So many things are not worth saying." I have not the presumption to pretend that I have a message to transmit, either in my own name or that of George, so why do I write? For myself? What a mockery! Action is worth so much more. What page (even written by oneself) could ever equal the sight of a shoal of fish disappearing into the haze in the direction of the open and the depths. I would gladly exchange everything that has ever been written on the sea, including Virgil and old Homer, for one single field of amphorae under sixty-five feet of water with little dark pomfrets eddying round them.

At times I feel inclined to confine myself to the scrappy notes of my diving diary which will be quite sufficient even in ten years' time to release my memories: "H—14, 25 on the bathymeter—south of the desert island—weather fine—rocky bottom. Old *mérou* still faithful at its post. Painfully shy sea-spider."

We are so much part of underwater life that we are apt to be surprised when we are not immediately accepted by our brethren down there. For a green lizard to fly from me on land leaves me unmoved, yet the flight of a little sea-spider is strangely annoying. "Idiot! I'm no longer a human. Can't you see that I am breathing under the sea?" I spent several precious minutes trying to drive it from its crack in the rock by tickling it, first with a sprig of sea-wrack, then with a stem of sea-fan, just as I used to do as a child with the crickets on the moor.

The *mérou* makes up for that. Every day I take it something to eat. I put the titbit on a rock, always the same one, give a long halloo that sends a stream of bubbles flying from the reducing-valve at the back of my neck, and then withdraw. Pompom (the fish) emerges from his hole, looks at me, hesitates—but every day a little less—then out he comes, the jutting pad on his lower lip brushing the plants. He comes for his pittance, swallows it greedily, forages round for a moment to be sure he has overlooked nothing, then retires scarcely any more quickly than he came. Every day I stay a little bit closer. I am sure that I shall manage to stroke him before we have to leave.

I should have liked to have done as the Romans did and to have tamed a muraena, but I have not yet seen one this year.

Back on land, heart glowing and body chilled, I can spend hours sitting dreaming on the warm rocks, still wearing my rubber frogmen's feet. At times I shut my eyes in an attempt to conjure up those marvellous pictures, and if I breathe a bit heavily in my excitement I can feel my softened eardrums expanding.

A few yards from the surface I can see George, for once without diving equipment, dozing inertly just under the surface with only the curve of his breathing tube showing. He is rather like a baby whale.

Two years ago we were not so familiar with the sea. The last time I stopped writing I had got as far, I think, as George's trial dive with our first really practical apparatus, when he went in from old Rebufat's boat just off the cove, and how, before that, Alan and his companions had rallied to us. In the evening after that double victory we are all rather exultant and noisy, all, perhaps, except George, who, I am sure, was already dreaming of fresh dives and greater depths. He must have been wondering, too, where we would go for them, for the little cove and its immediate surroundings would soon have no more to offer us. Perhaps we could take the boat and go on expeditions of two or three days. That would suit us, at any rate at the beginning.

*   *   *

The following Thursday, in token of our complete reconciliation, I was invited to Alan's for dinner. George was also invited, but for some reason or other he was unable to go. I was eager to make the closer acquaintance of our new friend.

I pulled the rusty handle of a bell by the low garden door and far away a cracked bell responded. Two or three minutes passed and then Alan himself opened the door.

We sat down for a few minutes on the hot coping of a little pool in the middle of the garden. Six feet away some big lizards were creeping about among some pots of thick-leaved plants standing beside a deserted chaise longue.

"Mother will be back soon. Come to my room, mean-while, it won't be so hot."

George, who always knows everything, had already warned me that Alan's father had died at sea in 1940, on board a trawler I believe. I noticed above Alan's bed the photograph of a naval officer with the traditional glasses

123

hanging on his chest. It could only have been his father. Alan saw that I was looking at it.

"I don't remember him," he said. "I was too young when his ship went down."

"You're like him," I said.

"Am I? You really think so?"

I realized that I could have said nothing that would have given Alan greater pleasure. His eyes were sparkling proudly and the words came tumbling out.

"I wish I could remember him. I try, and sometimes I think I can remember one day on his last leave when he took me on his knee and I amused myself by tugging at a decoration he had just been given. But I don't know whether I really do remember that, or whether I just think I do because I have been told about it . . . I'll show you something."

Carefully he took a polished wooden box from his wardrobe and opened it.

"It's his sextant. Isn't it beautiful? I'm beginning to know how to use it."

When we went down again Alan's mother had just come back and we found her lying in the chaise longue in the garden. She was friendly to me and spoke about Alan and the Scouts. Then she drew him to the chair and straightened one or two things about his clothes with a pale, long and rather limp hand.

"I hope," she said, "your group won't tire my son too much. He isn't too strong you know. Next week the doctor is going to start giving him a series of strengthening injections, isn't he, Alan?"

"Yes, mother."

"And, dear, please go and take your tonic, it's time . . ."

Alan gave an embarrassed smile and walked away. I went with him to the dining-room.

"It's silly," he said. "I'm really as strong as anyone, but, you know, mother is always afraid that I'm going to be ill. It was only because the doctor said it would do me good that she didn't make any difficulty about my rejoining the Scouts."

As he spoke, he filled a tablespoon with a thick, greenish syrup.

"If you don't think the stuff does you good, why do you take it?"

He shrugged his shoulders.

"For the same reason that I have the injections, the purges, the nasal drops, the thermogene—to please *her*, to reassure *her* . . . With father gone, you understand."

He emptied the spoon in one gulp, and his face contorted with disgust. Sympathetically I enquired:

"Is it really awful?"

"No, not at all really."

He reminded me of George swanking after his beating, but I would rather he had had a father's beating than his mother's potions. Didn't George once say that the Spartans used to take children away from their mothers at the age of eight. I was both moved by Alan's courage and irritated by his docility.

He put down the sticky spoon and corked the bottle of green syrup.

"Anyway I am getting used to it."

But I was not listening. I was trying to reconcile the spoon and the sextant.

*   *   *

The last few days before the summer holidays were devoted to intensive training of our new recruits, introducing the sons of solicitors, themselves probably future solicitors, to the splendours of new adventures.

It was not so easy with our material, inadequate and requiring careful handling as it did, and it meant that we had to shut our eyes to the possible consequences of sending down to depths of sixty feet little Scouts of thirteen and fourteen who without us would have been playing with a ball. Gradually, however, we perfected our methods: group-diving with someone on the surface with a life-buoy following the ascent of the bubbles and ready for accidents; a Davis gag to keep the mouthpiece in the mouth if an accident should occur, so that the person concerned did not breathe water before fainting; artificial respiration apparatus always ready, etc.

Some of the recruits took to it quickly, others not so quickly, others again could never manage it. One of these latter was our Alan. There was no denying that the initiative and moral courage he had shown in organizing the reunion with us was not matched by equal physical courage. Yet he was an excellent swimmer as he had shown that day when he swam back from the cove after we had taken his shoes; but the moment the mask was on his face and the heavy apparatus on his shoulders, cutting into them and emitting a slight filthy smell of hot rubber, he went to pieces and even before he was in the water got himself entangled in his frogmen's feet, the ones he had sent us. When the sea had closed over him I watched him through the window of my mask: he panicked. It was as though being submerged gave him a sort of vertigo. He swam with a breast stroke though flippers are made for a slow crawl and in the end he clung to the rock. That seemed to give him a little assurance, for he then moved slowly down it like some enormous crayfish, looking up occasionally at the surface with longing eyes.

As he was scarcely more than twelve feet down, I took a breath and went down to him, touched his shoulder and

pointed downwards with my thumb. However, he pretended not to understand, and clung on to the rock
feigning great interest in a very ordinary little algae. I
gave him a reassuring smile, then with a firm hand
suggested that he leave his rock, yet he just clung on
tighter. By then I had no breath left and had to go up.

When we got a second apparatus I was able one day to
take Alan down to thirty feet, holding him by the hand.
But that was a record. On another occasion there was
nearly an accident, for in a panic he had torn off both
mask and mouthpiece. Luckily Philip, who was escorting
him, hoisted him at once on to the life-buoy and from
there we got him back on board, livid in the face and
hiccoughing.

George to whom it was all so simple and easy was
completely unable to understand poor Alan.

"You wanted to dive. Well, you did. Are you, perhaps,
afraid?"

Alan blushed to the roots of his hair. When the poor
chap flung himself into our Adventure he certainly
could not have foreseen what it would cost him.

15

SUCH was the situation in the middle of July, when the whole troop left to go to camp. It was a real proper camp with a tall mast and the Scout Flag and our troop emblem flying from the yard.

At the foot of our site was a grotto with three entrances, its walls covered with spongiae and ascidians, one on top of the other. Once these had been free in the larval state, but now they were fixed to the rock and even when touched scarcely retracted their blue, mauve or cardinal-red cartilage. There were flowers on delicate saffron-coloured pistils, feathery plumes of the spirographes, soft yellow balls like toy chickens made of cotton wool, and, above all, concretions made up of thousands of animal-cules, and the delicate puckered, petrified petals of Neptune's lace.

If you could take your eyes from these microcosms, you saw on your right, beneath the dark vault, the light of the arch leading to the open sea. Above was a dancing shoal of sea-bream with forked tails, above that the silhouette of some nameless fellow diver also poised half way down the vertical slope with a cluster of escaping bubbles above him strangely dull against the light, and above that again was the limpidity of the blue-green sea, the sea, tall, deep and boundless.

Then your hand would open and release its hold and you would slowly drift towards the bottom, eyes closed and wishing that those minutes might never end.

Farther to the east, in the cove, among the tall rushes of the seaweed were the podgy shapes of some enormous

Preparing the boat before proceeding to make dives in deep water

Bubbles: to those on the surface they signal that all is well

sea-slugs. Farther east again, on the verge of another submarine grotto we encountered a strange creature like a violet handkerchief that suddenly unfolded and waved, and had a queer sort of snail's head at one of the corners. George said that it was a mollusc, a "sea hare". The ancients had used it like its brother the whelk, but while the latter yielded the purple of kings, the former had supplied them with a poison for the suppression of the politically undesirable.

We had new diving apparatus too, a Galeazzi made at La Spezia and some closed-circuit Pirellis designed for combat use.

I was very fond of those Italian closed-circuit masks which covered your entire face. Before going in you inserted at the bottom two little sponges which were meant to absorb any moisture that might seep in, and these always reminded me of the ones I used to have to wipe my slate at school.

Sometimes, around twenty-five feet, the respiratory bag would flatten gradually beneath the pressure and your fall would accelerate, but it only needed a tug on the release of the by-pass valve to start the hissing that made everything all right again. A puff of oxygen inflated the bag once more and your equilibrium was restored. How I loved gliding through the water then, as unobtrusive as a jellyfish and in utter silence, for there was not even the gurgling of a valve and no escaping bubbles to make a sound.

Then, perhaps, George beside me would make a sign and slowly we would start to rise, letting the oxygen filter through the corners of our lips. Back on the red rocks, we would close the inlet valve, connect the masks to the outside air, and have a few minutes' rest before going in again.

On either side of the peninsula, behind moles and torpedo-nets, were the calm, oily waters of the naval road-stead and the heavy grey shapes of cruisers, aircraft carriers and a pack of destroyers. Their steel sides sheltered hundreds of men, powerful intricate machinery, miles and miles of tubing painted in bright colours, glossy beneath the glare of the wire-protected lamps.

If war were to break out, in all the harbours of the world radar-scanners would begin their interminable gyrations, sweeping the sea as they sought to spot the enemy. Yet no dot would ever appear on the fluorescent screen to show the approach of a shoal of combat swimmers. By dead of night they would come; they would file through the nets, overcome all obstacles to reach the proud hulls. After some minutes of groping they would have accomplished their nefarious designs, and meanwhile, on the other side of the plates of steel, the crews would lie asleep in their hammocks beneath the blue night-lights, suspecting nothing.

Then there would be an explosion, the ship would shake from stem to stern, and there would be a rush of bare feet on the ladders. Slowly the tripod masts would tilt until there came the final act of turning turtle that would send the ooze from the bottom rising to the surface in heavy whorls.

"Ready?"

I replied to George's interrogative grunt by putting up my thumb. Then I opened the oxygen valve again and took hold of the bar of the tap beneath my mask. The artificial lung began to palpitate on my chest in time with my own breathing. Then the sea once more enfolded us.

* * *

The closed-circuit apparatus was not free from snags.

One morning the water seeped into a filter cartridge that was badly sealed, and while diving for the bottom Philip felt a mixture of salt water and soda lime flowing into his mouth. He surfaced at once. As the liquid was corrosive he wisely decided to rinse his mouth with vinegar and that soon cured the burns. Then, to cap it all, Claude fainted when using the same mask because we had gone too long without changing the soda lime. I suddenly saw him through the window of my mask lying to the left of me, motionless, his head on the bottom and his feet with their flippers up in the water. Naturally, George and I fished him up at once, and we hoisted him out and on to the jetty, water streaming from his cold body and his eyes turned up behind the round glass. I tore off the mask, as I had done with George five years before, and the rest of the equipment followed, as quickly as I could get it off. At that moment the rubber bag and those little bottles oxidized by the sea seemed so horribly fragile to have to stand up to the green water and those mysterious depths.

We laid Claud on a blanket, and he was kind enough to come to life again in about five minutes. The moment he did so, he was arguing with George about what had caused the accident. One thought it was due to the oxygen; the other attributed it to carbon dioxide, and they ended by getting quite heated in dispute.

That evening George read us some stories about combat swimmers from Ouvaroff's wonderful book. We remembered, too, what we had read in an English magazine some years before. Knowing the drawbacks of their apparatus, we had all the more admiration for the courage of those Italians who stole into enemy roadsteads with lips burned by soda lime and on their chests a little black rubber bag of oxygen which itself is toxic at high pressures. It goes without saying that, should there be another war, we intend to be combat-swimmers and serve in a destruction group, or a submarine mine-sweeping unit.

*   *   *

The sight of Claud lying there after his accident roused all Alan's terrors which had been subsiding. Afterwards I wondered that this reminder of death had not conjured up other pictures. As it was, he no longer had ignorance to shelter behind, and if he was to get himself into the water it could only be by the exercise of will. During the few hours before each dive I would see the fear mounting within him, a fear composed of mingled memories. He would no longer look you in the face and said little; or else he would go to the other extreme and be, falsely, sprightly for a while, until that gave place to gloomy thoughts. During the little ceremony of equipping the diver he would snatch at details, adjusting and readjusting the straps either to gain a few seconds, or perhaps also to concentrate his mind on purely material things.

*   *   *

The days of camp followed filled with dives, staged accidents, rescues and all sorts of exercises, such as removing the mask under water and putting it on again, voluntarily dropping the mouthpiece, disembarking at night from a rubber dinghy with your clothes on your back in a watertight bag. And in our tent-darkroom we were frantically busy developing our first underwater photographs. We had an exercise called the "Punch Bowl" which consisted of diving under a sheet of lighted petrol on the surface, after which you would see the shadows of your companions swimming as hard as they could beneath the glowing, roaring ceiling. And each evening we would gather round a great camp fire built among the rocks.

It gave me a lump in my throat when I thought how each of those beside me entrusted his life to me when I harnessed the apparatus on him, and I mine to them when it was my turn to dive. Exposed to the same risks we put ourselves in each other's hands, were responsible one to the other and closely linked by the dream we shared.

Scout Master Maurice had abandoned the helm and now seemed content to puff philosophically at his pipe, while George was our real leader. The troop's motto, a banal *ad astra*, had to be changed as that had now become slightly ridiculous. Philip had proposed that we should adopt a stylized siren and for motto *Non timemus*, (we do not fear (them) which was considered perfect as it would scandalise all the old Scout Commissioners.

Despite the undeniable attraction of the suggestion, we eventually adopted George's more ambitious motto "To the depths". George put his point in a voice vibrant with restrained enthusiasm: "no more stagnating in the old pseudo-techniques and little habits for employing body and mind; no more waiting for others to clear the way for us. With God's help, let us take our proper place, no longer in the wake or among the crowd, but straight ahead, like true Scouts; forward to Adventure and the Unknown; ours is the sea where it is widest and where it is deepest".

*   *   *

Just before camp George had made a watertight photographing box with an automatic interior pressure release that was linked to the evacuation circuit of the kamikaze. Because of this any accidental leak would not take the form of a catastrophic inrush of water, but by a string of bubbles that would act as a signal of damage. We used an old stereoscopic plate camera, and naturally it was not possible to change the plate underwater; George, however, maintained that by sealing the two lenses in turn with your hand it would be possible to get two different photographs, one on the right, one on the left of the same plate. We decided to make our first experiments in the cove at a depth of fifteen or twenty feet. George, wearing the full equipment, was to photograph first Philip and then me using the ordinary underwater hunting mask. George, very heavily laden, took up position lying on the bottom with the camera in its watertight box fixed level between two rocks. Philip went first, tilting and diving to the bottom, where he slowly wriggled in front of the lens like a fish caught by the gills. When my turn came, I held my breath, dived down and zigzagged towards George. I knew that I was to be ten feet from the camera, for the focus had been set at that beforehand with allowance made for the refraction of the water. I was almost in the correct position when George signalled to me to halt. Unfortunately, when I stopped swimming I began to rise towards the surface. Imperiously George gestured an order to descend, and of course to remain at the proper distance of ten feet. In the nick of time I managed to seize hold of a stone and started to sink again. I even managed to tilt a little over to the left and made one or two slight movements with my flippers which I hoped would look really graceful. I also tried to put on an expression of masculine assurance, but was rather hampered in this by the mouthpiece which puffed out my cheeks like a bull's-eye. Meanwhile George was fiddling furiously with his watertight box from which bubbles appeared to be ascending in considerable numbers. All was going beautifully, however, until just before

George released the shutter I unluckily dropped the stone which sent up fine sand swirling up into the calm water as it struck the bottom. George, I saw, had let go of his box, which was balancing at the end of its tube, being lighter than water, and he was shaking his fist at me violently.

Seen through the cloud of sand with all the annulated tubing waving round him George was like an irate devil-fish that had just discharged its ink. He was the one who should have been photographed. I felt a mad desire to laugh, accidentally swallowed a great gulp of salt water, and sent myself up towards the surface with one good kick.

When the plate was developed it transpired that Philip was blurred, while my picture, with only my face and feet appearing out of a solid screen, is one of our best under-water photographs. In fact, we have never taken a better, even with the ultra-modern cameras we now have. For a beginning it was a wonderful success.

Others of George's inventions unfortunately entailed greater risks, such as his famous watertight "combies" intended for use in winter. In order to give these a constant volume and overcome the risk of folds and wrinkles of hard rubber being forced into one's flesh by the increasing pressure, George had designed a contrivance for automatic inflation with acetylene gas obtained from the action of water on carbide.

On the morning of the trials Claud's father rang up and asked if we were aware that acetylene gas exploded spontaneously on reaching a certain pressure. Needless to say, we were not; and the thought of how near he had been to turning himself into an underwater mine made George sit down quickly.

* * *

Autumn came again and with it the equinox and bad weather. At the cove the frontier rock was black, while thirty feet above, at the level of the sea-green sky, the breakers made a thick canopy of moving clouds.

Winter brought long discussions by lamplight of future projects and things achieved, and our first experiments with watertight boxes for eight or sixteen millimetre cameras. Plans and memories were not enough however, and though George's inflatable combies had never materialized we made several trips to the ghastly, heaving sea. With forced smiles we tried to hide the physical agony of undressing in a squall and flying spray and then buckling the straps of the apparatus on to our shivering bodies. We had to slide in between two waves to gain the peace of the depths without damage; the cold was like a vice round our temples while we struggled to slow down our gasping breaths. In spite of it all we had some blissful minutes. Back on land, if we happened to have slipped once or twice against the rocks, we would see our various cuts and scratches bleeding profusely yet scarcely feel them because of the cold. It was a perpetual surprise. We were stupidly proud of these cuts and used to count who had the most; in fact we almost cherished them as the young Samurai did as they counted the wounds they received from fencing with sabres.

At last spring came and brought back light and warmth. It was then that for the first time we heard the name *Makassar*.

16

Poor *Makassar* disembowelled by two torpedoes, "innocent victim of the murderous folly of man," as our dear Scout Master, who has a passion for sententious pronouncements of the obvious, would probably have said if he had been able to go down to 130 feet to see it. Poor old ship to which I dived this morning for the fifth time this year, the ninth altogether. Half an hour before being torpedoed you were just an old panting ship, made to sail the seven seas at the minimum cost; but now, beneath the water, what silence and majesty there is about the confusion of what is left.

As I go down along the rope that we have bent to a large buoy—there being no longer any need for secrecy about her position—the details appear out of the haze in thoroughly illogical order: first a tangled mast-crane, then the gangway, a piece of the bridge, the bulwarks, the funnel; and then suddenly it all becomes a ship. It is like one of those music hall turns when an artist draws a number of seemingly unconnected lines and blobs, and then with one stroke of the chalk pulls them together and produces a picture. Poor old *Makassar*, but then I imagine that you are better off where you are, than rusting in some inner dock while waiting to be broken up.

It was one morning in the spring of last year that we first heard your name. Perhaps it was not even quite spring, but just the end of winter.

I might perhaps for the sake of a little romance and local colour pretend that our interview with the two pillagers of wrecks and V., the bankrupt fitter-out of ships, took place at the back of some room in an old shady tavern crowded with sailors and fishermen, with a parrot squawking "pieces of eight! pieces of eight!" from its perch, and a one-legged inn-keeper, but that would be to depart from the truth. It took place most prosaically in a bar with up-to-date chromium plating, not perhaps the best of places for us, considering our age, but then pilferers of wrecks do not usually frequent milk bars or teashops.

We took an immediate liking to the two wreckers. In our view the laws of man ceased to apply beyond the frontiers of our Marvellous Kingdom, so that what man has not been able to keep on the surface belongs to anyone brave enough to go down and get it. It would be a brave policeman who would try to stop us taking what we please beneath the sea.

One was called Leonard. He was an expert diver who made a regular habit of raiding the shelving sea-bed near the port, and who had acquired fame by penetrating inside a submarine that had been scuttled near Saint-Mandrier and removing all the optical equipment of the periscopes. The other, Voltrini, had made quite a little fortune officially by clearing mines, but in reality by salving—right under the nose of the Customs!—the tyres off jeeps in a sunken Liberty ship. That, of course, was less romantic than gold in Spanish galleons, but considerably more real.

Leonard had heard of our doings from old Rebufat, who apparently had been boasting about us. He and Voltrini and the bankrupt ship-fitter worked as a team, but as they were masked men and no longer able to do things with the necessary discretion, they had at once thought of us for the *Makassar*.

The very name, *Makassar*, had sounded exotic and full of promise. Poor old *Makassar*, promoted to your undoing to the rank of conveyor of divinities! And how strange altogether the fate of that statue the archaeologists know as the Cape Leuca Athene. I can still quote from memory the piece from the *Journal of Hellenic Studies* that V. showed us in order to tempt us:

"The statue of Athene Promachos which was recently fished up by a fisherman from Cape Leuca is without doubt one of the masterpieces of the age of Pericles. Although it is not possible to state it as a fact, it would seem that this statue, which is made of gold and ivory plates obtained from elephant's tusks by Sphyrelaton's secret process, ought to be attributed to the author of the Parthenon Athene. It was probably looted by Roman invaders and the galley taking it to Italy wrecked on the reefs of Cape Leuca at the very spot where the fisherman's nets caught in it by the most fortunate of chances. After the Cape Artemision Zeus and the survivor from the Bay of Marathon, that lovely bronze ephebe with head gracefully inclined, empty hands raised in some unknown task, or probably in some magical incantation, the sea has now with the Promachos Athene restored to man one of the purest masterpieces that has ever issued from under his hands."

I can imagine the departure of the cargo ship bound for Ostia or Brindisi, the loading of the statue to the rhythmical cries of the slaves as they hauled on the tackles, the sacrifice made to induce the gods to be favourable, and then the getting under way, the ornamented sail slowly dropping down the length of the mast and swelling out, the long oar that served as helm pivoting on the curve of the peak. Then one evening come the clouds and a wind that makes the ship heel over; ropes snap, the men start throwing the pot-bellied amphorae of the deck-cargo overboard in a vain endeavour to lighten ship; it is a true Virgilian storm, and then come the reefs.

Then, nearly two thousand years later, the statue was miraculously fished up again, having lain intact in the centre of the crumbling hull. Then come more wars and more invasions: the goddess is hastily put aboard the *Makassar* while bombs are falling on the port of Piraeus. And so the end, two torpedoes full in the side. What a queer history, and what a strange revenge Poseidon took on his old enemy Athene: lost, recovered, lost again.

When we came out of the bar, it had been raining hard. The wind made the hanging lamps creak as they swung and patches of light danced about the puddles. A group of ratings passed us, berets over their eyes, huddled in their pea-jackets. They were probably from the little mine-sweeper that had tied up that afternoon at the Belgian jetty.

"This business of the *Makassar* is a pretty funny affair", said George, pretending to be uneasy.

I was thoroughly excited and I knew that George in his heart of hearts was as happy as I at the adventurous turn things had taken.

* * *

The day following our meeting with Leonard and Voltrini we went to see V., the ship-fitter, in his office. He was alone. I can still see him as he stood there behind the model of *Makassar*, and I realize now that he was playing his last card. He concluded his instructions with an appeal for discretion.

Plenty of people knew of the precious cargo having been loaded into *Makassar*, so there was a risk of competitors appearing on the scene, as well as of ticklish questions of international law. We must be careful not to let ourselves be spotted by strangers, which was why it was impossible to organize a regular expedition with a proper ship and plenty of people.

Makassar, it was true, had gone off her normal course in an attempt to escape the submarines, and the site of the wreck was some distance from the traffic routes. In one way that was fortunate, but on the other hand it would mean that, if discovered, the presence of a salvage vessel in those parts would appear all the more remarkable. Our heads were buzzing with it all: the art of Phidias, the torpedoing of the *Makassar*, the statute of 1681 concerning the fishing up of wrecks and Greek artistic treasures looted by Roman invaders, etc.

I looked at the others. Alan's face wore an angelic smile; Claud's nose was puckered in thought over the technical problems of salvage, while Philip's eyes were sparkling, and round his mouth was the greedy expression of a Conquistador or a buccaneer getting ready to hoist the Jolly Roger.

As for George he seemed to find the whole thing perfectly natural, but strangely enough my imagination would not go beyond the second wreck. As easily as, without ever seeing them, I could picture long amphorae lying on the bottom, I just could not see the wonderful golden statue stretched in its case beneath 130 feet of sea-green water. To me it was incredible and quite incongruous: a gleaming helmet and shield, exact and classic, conceived for the sunshine of the Acropolis or the Parthenon, could not possibly be lying there in the play of the romantic gleams of light in the belly of a wreck. Yet there it was. The Cape Leuca Athene lay at the bottom of the sea like the statues of the Mahdia galley, those of the wreck at Cape Artemision, or the bronze youth with the extended empty hands fallen asleep beneath the waters of the bay of Marathon and now restored to the light of Athens.

Vague memories of mythology filled my mind. Old

Poseidon was keeping captive one who had dared dispute his empire with him, but we would rescue her, the heavy statue of gold.

For the statue was made of gold. That was the essential point as far as V. was concerned, and to some extent for us. For gold enables you to do things that are noble, which was probably what was in George's mind.

What a blow in the eye it would be for those who said that our experiments were useless and pointless! Our justification both to ourselves and to others would lie in this gold and the use we would make of it.

17

W E had decided to make a start about the middle of July, but bad weather delayed us until the twentieth. The two preceding months were the most feverish we ever had: we had to see to *Sagitta*, a tartan with an auxiliary motor which was being lent us by V., calculate the provisions and equipment we should need, arrange our ports of call, though our main preoccupation of course was our under-water equipment.

The first problem to be overcome was that of spotting the wreck. All the information, unfortunately meagre, V. had been able to give us was the approximate position of the desert island which had been "on the starboard bow" according to the log when the two torpedoes struck *Makassar* at 10.02 hours. Since the previous evening she had been navigating by dead reckoning and the numerous times she had changed course in the vain hope of escaping the submarines made her position all the more uncertain. We foresaw difficulties.

Our short experience of diving had filled us with admiration for those divers who, if they are to be believed, at the very first or second descent dropped right on to the galleon with its cargo of gold which they had located on the strength of some old *portolan* map or the account of a pirate captain.

We, it is true, were dealing with a big wreck, nearly two hundred feet long; almost intact, and so recent that it could not have had time to become embedded in the sand or mud of the bottom. It was true, too, that our pumping apparatus would allow us to go down as often as we pleased. However, we needed to act quickly so as not to arouse unhealthy curiosity about what it was we were fishing for.

It was then that the ever-watchful George read in a newspaper article about an engineer, Jayet's "diving rudder", which was a sort of under-water aquaplane that was towed by a boat and which allowed the diver both to manoeuvre rapidly and to explore large submerged areas without fatigue. Apparently it had been used with great success for finding amphorae, the stocks of antique anchors and generally for all archaeloogical remains that are scattered about the immense floor of the sea. Apparently, too, the specialists of the Submarine Study and Research Group in *Elie Monnier* used a similar device for locating the wreck of the Mahdia galley.

We plagiarized ruthlessly. Our apparatus, streamlined like a wing or whip-tailed sting-ray, carried embedded in it a compass filled with glycerine to counteract the pressure, a bathymeter, a thermometer and a watch in a watertight case. On the following edge we painted a spectroscopic strip to show the modifications of the light in terms of depth.

We made our first trial in a canal. Not yet having a boat at our disposal we towed the aquaplane from the towpath using a motor-bicycle borrowed from Claud's father's garage and with Claud riding it. George, who was always our guinea-pig, was to wear just the ordinary mask with tube and come up from time to time to breathe on the surface. He christened the trials, "Operation Brunehaut", and though he did not suffer the fate of that unfortunate princess, his adventure was no less dramatic. When, at the end of one hundred and fifty yards of towing, with the canal foaming and the motor-bicycle spluttering on the towpath, we fished George out, it was to find him

stark naked, tube, mask and even his bathing pants
having been swept off him by his speedy passage through
the water. We hastily handed him a towel which he
draped round him like a *pareo* and climbed with the
dignity of a Tahitian chief on to the bank among a little
crowd of watermen and dumbfounded persons out for a
walk.

After that, to avoid future denudations, we designed a
special mask (an unbreakable glass vulcanized on to the
rim of a gas-mask that encompassed the entire face) and
regretfully decided that we must considerably reduce the
speed at which we towed the aquaplane.

A fortnight after the first trial we were ready again and
were able to carry out the first tests at sea.

George's adventure in the canal had left him with an
infected sinus and he was not allowed to dive for a month,
so I was the guinea-pig for the sea trials. George started
the boat's motor and I took up position on the little
beach, holding the aquaplane in both hands, artificial lung
on my chest, my face covered with the special mask and
up to my knees in water. The thin white tube that linked
me to the pumps was fastened at intervals to the towing
rope. Silently I rendered thanks to Heaven for George's
sinus.

Suddenly the towing rope went taut and I flung myself
horizontal. For a few seconds, while the aquaplane had its
nose up, I skimmed the surface in a smother of foam, then
with a simple press of the hands on the rubber grips I
inclined the wing downwards and began diving at an
angle of thirty degrees. In the U-shaped tube of the
bathymeter the reading went up swiftly: 7, 8, 9, reached
the top and started down the other side, but more slowly
now as the graduation became closer. Although I had had
a generous injection of ephedrine my ears were beginning

to hurt a bit. At fifty feet I flattened out level with the seaweed. The rope with the white tube looking like a string of macaroni curved in a parabola up to the surface. The air was arriving irregularly; I could hear it flowing into the bag at intervals with a great sigh from the non-return valve. No doubt the tube, being curved by the speed, had a kink in it at one of the fasteners; but that did not worry me. I knew that with one movement I could rear up and bound up to the liquid sky, perhaps shoot out into the air like a flying fish.

Suddenly the ground dropped away, one thrust and I was following it downwards, hands clenched on the grips and the aquaplane vibrating and twisting as though it were trying to escape. Sixty-five feet. I was skimming the ground that was tufted with weed. A little more pressure of the hands and I was lower still. Then, my speed reduced, I forced my way like an enormous ray through the rushes. The frontal edge of the thick wing swept the flexible spikes apart, but I could feel them closing in again and running, whippy and cold, all along my thighs and legs to my motionless flippered feet. First it was jungle, then bush, then suddenly I emerged over a stretch of bare sand. The rope disappeared into the haze above me. The water was suddenly cold and I went up a few feet to get out of the cold layer.

More rocks covered with vegetation emerged out of the haze, were beneath me, then behind. But, as I swept by, I still had time to notice some big green star-fish, a startled octopus making off on the starboard bow and being brushed by the plane and unfolding like a miserable parachute; also a shoal of fish disintegrating and dispersing in a mad explosion in all directions. The bubbles of my respiration, trailing behind like the plume of a locomotive, must have been left far behind, where slowly they would mount, swaying towards the surface. At intervals a long shiver would pass through the wooden wing. My hands closed more tightly round the moulded rubber grips; I seemed to be holding a live creature, some mythological fish sent us by benevolent gods to permit us to plumb the realm of Glaucus and Thetis. The watery wind caressed my face by the quivering fringe of the mask, enveloped me, draping my naked body with a swirling cloak of sea-green water, and the touch of it on shoulders, back and limbs was like a divine caress. When you are not yet sixteen, it rather goes to your head when you find yourself driving the chariot of the god Poseidon.

* * *

We felt sure that with the aquaplane we would be able to comb the bottom and locate the wreck without much difficulty. But that done, we still had to get down to the wreck, go inside and work there. The kamikaze with its two hand pumps would scarcely get down to 130 feet, except perhaps for just a moment or two, and that put any difficult or lengthy operation out of the question. Also, we did not see anything very attractive about the idea of plunging into the darkness through broken, sharp steel plates dragging a tube the thickness of one's finger behind us. It was obvious that we would have to have autonomous equipment with bottles of compressed air. Unfortunately our finances would not run to a Cousteau apparatus. This time it was Claud Walter, not George, who found the solution.

The town fire brigade possessed an old respirator for dealing with toxic gases which was no longer used. It consisted of a copper gladiator's helmet, copper rear-peak and, strapped to your back, two massive cylinders of grey steel which discharged a continuous flow of fresh air into the helmet by means of a reducing valve. The fire brigade was only too glad to let us have it; but naturally, even admitting that such a contraption had been capable of saving a fireman's life twenty years ago, there was no guarantee that it would be able to save us from drowning now. Claud had the idea of fitting a big demand valve to it, and this we did using one intended for motor-car engines converted to run on gas. This was a large box of thick metal with a flexible framed membrane for a lid. Each inhalation the diver took created a depression in the closed chamber of the helmet, causing the membrane to sag. It was this movement which, through the plate, automatically opened the gas feed, which remained open throughout the inhalation, thereby releasing the exact amount of air necessary. The moment inhalation ceased, the box filled, the flexible lid rose and closed the needle-valve, thus preventing any unnecessary discharge beyond the period of inhalation.

To make this device work under water we had replaced the return-spring with a slightly more powerful spring taken from an Eureka pistol; this we hoped would prevent the difference in pressure from opening the membrane and so causing a continuous discharge. We also reinforced the rubber-cloth of the membrane with two thicknesses of waterproof nylon material. We were very proud of ourselves.

The apparatus had no reserve device, however, so, in order that we should know when to go up and not be caught with empty cylinders under 130 feet of water, Claud designed a gauge which was at the end of a rigid pipe that followed the line of the body and passed under the armpit, so that you could read it when submerged. Neither Philip nor I liked the idea of that gauge: suppose it neglected its duties and went on telling you that there was plenty of air left? To Claud the possibility did not even exist, and all that George, the latinist, would say was: *"Fortuna audaces juvat, adjutorium nostrum in Nomine Domini"*, which was a fine mixture of the sacred and the profane, and that, to be on the safe side, he, George, would dive first.

The new apparatus and the prospect of testing it kept George wildly happy for the three weeks before the actual day. Untried apparatus meant not only a new key to our Marvellous Kingdom, but another taste of the delicious pangs of the first dive, of not knowing the extent of the risk you were running; while the slight alterations to be made in the way you breathed in and out, the ease of movement, were all things that provided a new sensation, such as I imagine a crustacean must feel after shedding its shell.

When the great day came I was in bed with 'flu and almost beside myself at not being able to escort George down to ninety feet with the kamikaze or else with mask and tube on the surface.

"George, I've got an awful feeling that . . ."

"Don't be a fool. You're a bit feverish still. You'll see, shortly after tea the door will open and in we'll come, and we'll tell you all about it. Anyway, what's going to happen to me?"

"I don't know. The gauge might stick."

George laughed and began playing the fool, gagging about nitrogen narcosis and the other pleasant things that might happen. I could get nothing more whatever out of him.

"Well, I wish it was this evening and it was all over."

"I don't", said George, becoming serious again. "This waiting with the adventure always at the back of your mind, even when you are thinking of other things; this combination of threat and promise, fear and hope, is a sort of reflection of our destiny."

My wait, however, was not like George's, and I shall never forget it. All afternoon I waited, listening for doors to open, cars to draw up. Tea was almost over. Some woman visitor departed. George ought to be here soon, I thought, he said he would. Evening was falling and the lamps lit up; then I heard the bell and my heart gave a leap of joy; it could only be George. But it wasn't George. It was the woman visitor coming back for her umbrella which she had forgotten. The words of the book I was reading had ceased to make any sense; I was getting into a fever of suspense. I could see George, the apparatus strapped on to his back like a great rucksack, putting the mouthpiece between his teeth, straddling the side of the boat, disappearing . . .

Perhaps the gauge had stuck, or George had succumbed to nitrogen narcosis. Often he had spoken to me quite bitterly of this dangerous feeling of well-being that can come over the diver at depths below 130 feet and which is attributed to the slow fixation of a certain quantity of nitrogen in the tissues; this strange phenomenon deprives you of your sense of direction, makes you quite indifferent to the idea of death and even destroys any desire you may have to go back to the surface.

That morning I had had a horrid presentiment; but George was one of those who conquer, as he had so often done already; he was like one of those Greek heroes whom some divinity protected, and always preserved miraculously at the last moment.

It was eight o'clock and no one had come. Dinner arrived on a tray. There was a great lump in my throat. I knew now that something had happened. The door opened. Surely it was George. No, it wasn't. It was the doctor.

"Getting on nicely, but there's still a little fever. . . ."

Steps on the stairs. Could it be he? I hadn't heard the bell. Perhaps he had come in as the doctor went out. Then the sound of George and Alan's triumphant voices:

"One hundred and seventy feet, Francis! A hundred and seventy. But at the point we chose there was a devilish current. We had to go on sounding elsewhere till five o'clock. And, you know, I thought I was going to die . . ."

Here my tragic expression caused a bellow of laughter.

". . . there was such a crush in the tram on the way back."

The tension over, we could all enjoy ourselves. To symbolize our good fortune we baptized the apparatus "Felix" (the cat) and we painted his picture on the port cylinder.

Scout Master Maurice called upon our services for the annual festival of the Scout Group. This meant exhibiting ourselves on the stage of the municipal theatre in bathing slips, strung with our artificial lungs and high-pressure bottles, waddling from one foot to the other till we reached the centre of the stage and then awkwardly fiddling with our equipment so that we did not look too great fools among the painted scenery and in the shadow-less glare of the footlights. We felt thoroughly ridiculous and out of place, all except George, who peacocked like an old duck in front of the farmer's wife arriving with its food.

Our Scout Master gave the public a rather learned, technical dissertation which contained a bit of everything: nitrogen narcosis, oxygen intoxication and pulmonary rupture. What irritated me most was the way he tapped the steel cylinders with the air of a conqueror and

exclaimed: "Thanks to this equipment *we* have been able
to go down to one hundred and ninety-five feet." And he
had never even got his head under with an ordinary fishing mask!

As soon as we could we hopped off the stage and away.
George was inclined to be indulgent and said that at least
the Scout Master was now becoming interested in the
question.

That interest, however, did not survive the Scout
festival. Before leaving for our desert island we asked the
Scout Master whether our Scout insurance covered us
against possible accident while diving, and we were told
that it did not. George was livid, not because of the £150
to be paid in the event of death, but as a matter of principle.
We realized then, of course, that the Scout Master would
never countenance diving elsewhere than on the stage of
the municipal theatre.

After that we wrote direct to the Scout Headquarters in
Paris and eventually they agreed to cover us. Then,
reassured by the financial consolation promised to our
families, we decided to start operations as soon as
possible.

On 12 July we embarked three two and a half gallon
high-pressure cylinders for recharging those of the
autonomous apparatus, "Felix's feeding bottles" as Philip
called them. However, the mistral was blowing in great
long gusts, so we went to consult old Rebufat. For once
he did not mention his little cloud. His verdict was truly
oracular:

"As far as the wind goes, I advise you to set out; but as
far as the sea goes . . . my advice is: do not go."

Although both Claud and George had elected to do
their service in the Navy when the time came, we had not
much confidence in ourselves as sailors, and so we waited

philosophically for the wind to drop at any rate below force four.

*   *   *

At last came the day of our real departure, our D-day.

Right up to the last moment it had been assumed that Alan was not coming with us, but a chance remark the doctor made to his mother about the beneficial effects of the sea decided her to entrust him to us. He was suitably overjoyed, but I still felt that he was torn between dread of his physical fear and the desire to grapple with it in real earnest.

We were to set out at dawn, and by the evening before we had finished transporting our material and equipment and were assembled in George's room. There, with a sort of melancholy enthusiasm, we divested ourselves of our everyday clothes and sent them flying across the room: shirts with hard collars and cuffs, waistcoats and ties; then we put on the heavy garments of naval uniform that were altogether too large for us: trousers of rough cloth and striped jerseys. It was like putting on a new skin, becoming a different person, without past, without ties or social constraints, like escaping from a caste and a civilization that stifled us and for which we no longer had any taste. Later, when we had undergone the change several times, we took to calling George's room the "flooding-chamber" from which, like those imprisoned in the vitiated air of a sunken submarine, we could escape once we had equipped ourselves, merely by opening the door.

At dawn we walked down to the harbour. There was a smell of iodine in the warm air, as if the sea had come to meet us. Behind the walls of the houses slept those who either did not know how, or did not wish, to be off and

153

away. Our sandals clattered in the empty streets and our trousers twined round our legs. We thrust our fists deep into the pockets of our pea-jackets and felt joyously resolute. We were a little self-conscious in our unusual get-up, but we were triumphantly free, and in our mind's eye we could already see the splendours to come.

18

I HAVE re-read what I wrote yesterday and I suppose that logically I should now go on to describe that first trip out to the island, but I do not feel much inclined to do that, because we have very little of which to be proud.

We got away from the quay by hauling on the booms of our neighbours, and we did not dare start the motor till we were in open water. With his usual cheek George pretended that the helm was bad, and, once at sea, he told us too that the compass did not seem to be functioning as it should. We got over this by hugging the coast and by hailing two steamers we met and asking them our position.

But let us leave these embarrassing details, especially as I am in a hurry to get to the desert island and the wreck of *Makassar*, in a hurry to get back in my tale to the familiar surroundings of our second expedition, the grey and red rocks which the setting sun colours mauve, the little shingly beach, the crater, sheltered from the wind, at the bottom of which sobs a little spring, and thirty feet away the wooden cross marking the grave of the unfortunate sailor of *Galathea*. Last year, when we saw our island for the first time, George at once saw the possibilities of the sheer cliffs and I saw him smile in pleasurable anticipation at the thought of the giddy slopes that would continue down from the surface.

In order to be sure of my facts, this morning at breakfast I made Philip go over the details of how he located the wreck last year. For four days we had been vainly combing the sector north-east of the island, one of us on the aquaplane under water, two at the pumps, and the fourth at the helm. We were beginning to get discouraged when suddenly we saw the placer-buoy leap out of the water. "I was slap over it," Philip had told me that morning, "and went straight through between the masts as though I had been wanting to machine-gun the decks, almost level with the funnel. I was so overcome that I was two or three seconds late in releasing the buoy."

We at once fixed the spot by going down and tying a rope to the mast and with it mooring a discreet little buoy.

* *

We had our doubts all the same. Suppose it was not the right wreck, a different boat altogether?

That evening as we sat by our camp fire, George, plan in hand, interrogated Philip for the tenth time.

"You are quite sure? A large bridge, and fairly far back a dumpy funnel?"

"But, of course, quite sure. I did not see it for long, but I had it in full profile."

On the plan George's finger traced a mysterious itinerary between the black strokes of the bulkheads and the water-tight compartments down to a little red mark. Again and again his finger went back to this red mark beneath the bridge, for that was the famous packing-case containing the statue which we were to get up to the surface whatever it cost.

* * *

Now, being equipped with the most modern apparatus that lets us penetrate without fear, risk or difficulty into the intimacy of the wreck as often as we like, we remember the difficulties of a year ago with a certain amount of bitterness. If we had had our present equipment then! But it's too late now.

The sea was not kind to us either. The day after locating the wreck, one of the pumps fell overboard into forty feet of water and down we had to go in a free dive to look for it; and while we were still on the beach, the south wind flung spray in our faces like shouts of defiance.

And these Japanese gardens with their unreal iridescent colours that this year we can admire without hurry or fear through the windows of masks that are filled with fresh air, are they really the chaotic jungle that we used to sweep through while suffocating beneath 150 feet of angry, leaden sea? And the wreck itself, that we can now flood with all-revealing light, too geometrical to be a rock, centre of luxuriant life where we now gather plants, is that really what we used to touch gropingly at the end of our dive, while behind the misted glass of our masks, our eyes, already blurred by the first symptoms of asphyxia, seemed to see phantom shapes? That was a year ago, when we made those four dives. Four, that was all.

We decided to use the apparatus with the two pumps for examining the wreck and to reserve the compressed air of the autonomous equipment for the final assault on our objective.

According to the plan the easiest route seemed to be to go in via the hatchways from the bridge, but when George got back from a dive that lasted three-quarters of an hour, he told us that there was nothing doing in that direction. It was easy enough to get under the upper bridge, but after that the way was obviously blocked by debris and collapses. There remained the two breaches made by the torpedoes, and it was my job to go down and examine them the following day.

All that I can find in my diving diary about it is this:

"17 August. Dived at 13.40 hours on wreck M. Down 130 feet. Slight nose-bleed. Surfaced at 14.25 hours after twenty minutes decompression at ten feet."

A quarter of a mile out from the shore the swell caught us on the beam and we began to roll horribly. Shortly afterwards I found myself slightly insensitive to outside sensations and wondered, horror-stricken, whether I was going to have my first experience of being seasick. Luckily we could already see the top of the buoy emerging every now and again from the short waves straight ahead of us. Then, while George moored the boat, I put on the equipment as quickly as I could. It was beginning to rain and I looked at the grey, opaque water with a certain distaste. But after all the air was being delivered all right, so I stuck up my thumb.

Coldness clasped my body, a wave swept over my head, then the sea closed over me. The plume of bubbles rising from the valve swayed and twisted in time with the swell, and the rope that led vertically down into the greeny-blue depths quivered beneath my fingers that were already numb.

At fifty feet I stopped, holding on to the taut rope with one hand. There were no waves down there, and what silence and peace. But it was dim already, for the commotion on the surface broke up the rays of light, so that they became diffused in water that was laden with minute particles in suspension. On my left, the silver plume of bubbles now rose up straight, like a jet of luminous steam in the obscurity of the water. Then I lowered my head and stared stupidly at my ghastly legs that ended in large frogmen's feet. For a few seconds I amused myself moving my legs for the pleasure of seeing the flippers bend rhythmically beneath the heavy pressure of the water. The bottom was still invisible. On the ceiling of crumpled cellophane above me was the black shadow of the boat dancing at the end of the rope. Swallowing my saliva, I continued on my way down. It was cold. There was a grey shadow, and all at once it had come into focus: *Makassar*! I could only see bits through the haze, and at first sight it looked just a lot of old iron.

Jade green streaks across the window of my mask were making it difficult to see. Some little blood vessel must have burst under the pressure; I was bleeding a little from the nose. The density of the water having long since halted the red rays, the drops of my blood looked green as they spread across the thick safety-glass that lay between my eyes and that vast aquarium.

I let go of the rope and dropped softly on to the bridge, sending up a spurt of mud and slime.

Must I go lower yet, below 130 feet, down to where the keel lay embedded on the sand of the seabed? To be candid I had no desire to do so, and I decided to make another attempt on the passage in from the bridge. My artificial lung was filling badly. I was too heavily weighted and moved from one hatchway to the other with the heavy flight of a tired octopus. There was nothing doing.

The black night of the wreck repulsed me as much as the sharp corners and cutting edges of the torn plates. Still I hesitated on the bridge. I wanted to stay there if only for a minute, before embarking on what was the real adventure, but in my mind's eye I could see George's face as he bent over the pressure gauge of the buffer bottle, biting his lips at the way the trembling needle remained stubbornly at the figure 30. I swallowed a gulp of air, let the lung fill itself again, put my legs over the slimy fence of the bulwarks and dropped slowly down the vertical side that grated beneath my white fingers. In the visibility that was now reduced to a few yards all I could see of the wreck was this severe black rock-face which would never sport any of those marvellous flowers. My hands, sliding down, felt the dip of a port-hole, fastened on the step of the bilge keel, and after that the face curved inwards, receding from my hands, so that I had to use my feet to keep myself against it. Above me the liquid sky had gone and there was not even a haze bathed in a diffuse light. All I could see was the mass of the overhanging ship's side like the roof of a cave. The air from the pumps was only reaching me in a thin trickle that I sucked in in hurried little inhalations, as though afraid that it would suddenly dry up. Instead of the streaming plume that issued from the valve at the side of the artificial lung when at a depth of fifty feet or so, all that now came was an intermittent meagre puff of bubbles that went trickling up the black side, hung for a moment at the bilge keel, then freed themselves and rose on, up towards the light.

There was the first breach. It was just at the seat of the tail-shaft bracket and extended to the right, level with the sand, as far as the screw itself which was like a dark enormous flower with slimy petals lying in the Chinese shadow of the run of the ship's bottom.

* * *

It was then that I felt afraid, more afraid that I have ever been before. For a fleeting moment the artificial lung went flat against my chest; desperately I inhaled air that was not there; with a thrust of my heels I sent myself upwards. I bounced on the overhang of the barnacled hull as I went up, caught on the bilge keel, my mask became displaced and began to leak. I thrust myself away and was free.

By rising I had reduced the pressure and that released

the air which began to fill the artificial lung once more. Again a comforting stream of bubbles was streaming from the valve, but I had lost the rope and was following the thin thread of my white breathing tube through the haze. With great thrusts of my flippered feet I hoisted myself up and up towards the light despite the heaviness of my weighted belt. The artificial lung was like a balloon on my chest and the hiss of air escaping from the top of the valve was growing more and more violent, while every now and then the star-shaped safety-valve on the bag itself rose up and dribbled out a few enormous bubbles shaped like mushrooms. My bubbles preceded me as well as accompanied me.

At ten feet below the surface the stirrup hanging at the end of its rope was weighted, and on it I sat, straddling it like a trapeze, while I waited for the decompression stage to take its course. George would pull me from the boat when the time was up. I began wondering how I was going to tell him that I had been afraid.

In front of the others George called me "sissy", "aquarium diver" and only fit for "the Pope's navy", and added that in the morning he would go down and have a look at the breach himself. It was most mortifying and he and I did not speak all that evening. Then, just before we turned in, George put his hand on my shoulder and with his great, disarming smile said:

"Angry with me?"

I drew my shoulder away:

"Yes, I am."

His face dropped at that and he looked so unhappy that I could not help smiling in my turn.

"No, I'm not any more now, but I assure you that the air was not coming."

George's face clouded, for it is a failing of his never to

admit that *his* material can be at fault. I thought I might as well be conciliatory.

"At any rate I had the impression that the air wasn't coming", I said, and we left it at that.

*   *   *

Alan never overcame his funk, and I leave you to imagine what George, who was hard enough on me and especially severe in his demands on himself, thought of him. Poor Alan! He was too proud to pass his turn to dive, yet a sort of panic seemed to come over him each time he reached the level of the wreck's bridge with its litter of debris, and his window showed him nothing but riven plates of steel. We would see the needle of the gauge on the buffer-bottle drop and a gush of bubbles would break the surface. George, leaning over the gauge, his forelock drooping in front of his eyes, would go pale with anger and disgust:

"Thirty feet! Ye Gods, he's coming up already!"

Then a head would appear in the midst of the foam and behind the glass of the mask I would see Alan's haggard eyes. As he hoisted himself painfully into the boat George would curse and swear at him, calling him every name under the sun, and even Claud, Philip and I would feel a surge of anger. If he must do it, why not be like everyone else.

At first, Alan would sit shivering on the bottom of the boat apparently insensitive to the insults being heaped upon him, but then as he began to recover from the cold of the depths and the nausea of fear, his cheeks would flush and I could tell by the tightness of his lips that he was having difficulty in restraining tears of shame.

It was, I think, because he reminded us of our own fear, that we were so hard on Alan. Without him we would have forgotten it; but with him there in the flesh it was like a reincarnation of our fear, a demon of fear grinning at us, and we had to do something to defend ourselves, so we ridiculed it to keep it from laying hold of us in our turn.

At night, in the tent, Alan would sometimes be in tears. Being next to him I was the only one to know it. I badly wanted to console him, to tell him that we were all very fond of him, but it would not do. Alan had to work out his own salvation, by his own will, just as a year before he had joined us of his own accord.

I used to wonder too how far the *Makassar* reminded him of another wreck, this time in the troubled waters of the North Sea, but I could not speak of that either, for to put that horror into words would have been to make it more distinct than it perhaps was in his imagination.

All I could do was to pray for him, be as nice to him as possible on shore and in the intervals between our dives, for I realized that the next day, or the one after, when he again came up too quickly, his face ugly with fear, I would not be able to prevent myself looking at him with an expression of contempt. I decided, however, that I would speak to George about it. His reply was to quote from his beloved T. E. Lawrence, something to the effect that every deserter is a potential V.C.; and he added in a gentle voice:

"You don't think that I don't like him, do you?"

"But while waiting for Alan to earn his V.C., you must admit we are insulting him more and more."

*   *   *

The next day George went down as he had said, and that was the day he very nearly had a nasty accident. For an hour he had been taking turn about at the pumps, the needle of the gauge on the buffer-bottle swinging slowly between 30 and 40, and then suddenly it began to drop swiftly: 25 ... 20 ... 15 ... 10 ... We thought at first that the air tube must have broken, but it was not that. George himself could never say exactly how his weighted belt had come loose when he was at 120 feet, ten feet from the bottom. Perhaps it had not been properly fastened before he went in, or perhaps he had caught it on a sharp corner when he was not paying attention. Whatever it was, he was suddenly relieved of the weight of nine pounds of lead and shot up towards the surface.

"I realized the situation perfectly", George told us. "My first thought was of the possibility of pulmonary explosion caused by dilation of the air in the artificial lung and in my own lungs; but then I thought that perhaps the duck-bill valve and the safety-valve together would let out enough to evacuate all surplus air before I got to the surface. But then there was gaseous embolism which I could get from not observing the stages of ascent and from too rapid decompression, because I had been almost an hour between 100 and 120 feet down. As I passed I tried to catch hold of the bulwarks, but I just missed them and saw the superstructure dwindling and disappearing in the haze. It felt as though I were being winched up at lightning speed, and stupidly I moved my arms as though to clutch the empty water.

"At about fifty feet I found the solution. Using both arms I crushed the lung that was ballooning on my chest like a great buoy. An enormous mushroom of bubbles came from the safety-valve. I had no mark to judge by, but it seemed that I was no longer rising so quickly. Then I felt the impact of little bubbles that I had outdistanced in my climb and which were now catching me up and enveloping me in glistening draperies. Frantically I tried to squeeze the last of the air out of the folds in the bag. I exhaled deeply and emptied my lungs as well as I could, and compressed my thoracic cavity as far as I was able in order to reduce my buoyancy still further. I had a distinct sensation of being suspended in a sort of unstable equilibrium between life and death, death being in the direction of the surface and the sun, and life, oddly enough, towards the cold of the bottom. For a moment I thought of doing a duck-dive and sending myself straight down by using my flippers, but I was afraid that if I did that I would let go of the artificial lung and that it would swell and take me up again. As it was, I had it squeezed almost flat and was content to breathe the life-giving air in small amounts, being terrified lest I should swell and start rising again. Then my heart gave a bound: it was all right; *Makassar* was appearing again. With the pipes of the apparatus emptied of the air that had been pulling me to the surface like a magnet, the mere weight of it was sending me slowly down like a docile Cartesian diver. Then I reached the bulwarks, the port-holes; and slowly, as in a dream, the black riven side came towering up. I was back in my own comforting universe. There was the grey smudge of the bottom and already I had my eye on some pieces of rock lying on it."

With these bits of rock under his arm to ballast him George had been able to let the artificial lung inflate itself again and he had then continued exploring the breach. He found his weighted belt and buckled it round his waist, after which he was able to dispense with the pieces of rock, and in the end he had returned gradually to the surface without further incident.

With George's usual taste for euphemism and discreet blowing of his own trumpet this incident became "a nasty episode, fortunately overcome by the exercise of intelligence."

That evening, when the others had already gone to the tent, George and I stayed on for a short while watching the firebrands die. I raised my head once and looked at George, his face a patch of light and his pale hands lying on the brown of the rug like strange animals. I thought how he might so easily have been cold and stiff, wrapped in canvas and ready to be laid to rest near the little spring, alongside the sailor from *Galathea*. Was he thinking of that too? He seemed to me more precious for having been so nearly killed, to have a nimbus of the mysterious aura that those have who have been right to the limits. I wondered if he would tell me anything more. Our eyes met and he smiled.

"People say that at moments like that you always see your parents, your friends, your past, your sins, etc., in a sort of close-up. I didn't see a thing. When I took off and, on the way up, especially after I had missed the bulwarks, my thoughts were all of the accident, of the present. After crushing the bag, I was curious to see whether I was going to go down again, and then, too, I had rather a queer thought. I was almost in equilibrium between the top and the bottom. At the surface, in the air and the sunshine, beside you all, was death as far as I was concerned, while life was down below in the blackness, the cold and the pressure. Queer. And I remembered then that fish the *Lacaze-Duthiers* brought up in her trawl last summer. When it reached the surface it was dead from decompression, had sort of burst, rather like I would have, if I had gone straight on up to the surface.

"I thought about that fish right until the superstructure of *Makassar* began to emerge again, and then I realized that no trawl was taking me up to the surface and that I was saved.

"But perhaps I only had those thoughts because I was

not really going to die. The day I am really for it, no doubt there will be signs, a cortège of demons and angels, and then I ought to see all my past."

"Will you be afraid to go down again?"

George gave a great laugh:

"Indeed no. On the contrary, I know now that whatever happens to me, like Ulysses, I will always find some ruse that will cheat Hades at the last moment."

19

WHEN there was too much of a sea to let us go out to *Makassar*, we stayed on shore and either fished or looked for shell-fish. One morning I was busy collecting among the pools and rocks of that part of the island off which the wreck lay. I had a dagger the point of which I used to thrust under the shell before the creature inside had time to retract and seal itself to the rock. All at once I raised my head and listened. I could hear a dull reverberant sound as though the sea had struck a gigantic gong somewhere beneath my feet. It sounded as though there must be some fault in the rock through which the water kept sweeping, so, abandoning my search for barnacles, I went to fetch my mask and frogmen's feet. The waves kept knocking me against the rocks that were covered with violet and brown sea-urchins and I could not get a proper position, so I went out a little way and came in again diving under when I was fifteen feet or so out. It was as I had thought: there was a narrow, vertical, open fault in the rock marbled with red algae and almost blocked by anemones, whose tentacles swayed this way and that in unison, keeping time with the surge of the waves. The fault widened out at the base and became the mouth of a cave thirty-five or forty feet below the surface. In need of breath I surfaced, but, having located it, I was now able to keep my eyes on the mouth of the cave. It was like a gaping mouth in a tousled beard of mauve anemones. I rose and fell with the waves, and as I did so it retreated into the haze or rose up to meet me. It was fascinating.

The next morning, when the sea was a bit calmer, we were able to go inside the fault using our pumping apparatus; and this morning, one year later, I have been back and made a tour of *my* cave. It has not changed.

I slipped slantwise through the narrow slit like a submarine window, the two cylinders of the Cousteau apparatus just going through, and then, with my arms along my sides and preceded by my bubbles, I sent myself up the long vertical tunnel with slight movements of my flippers until I emerged in the vaulted chamber with its luminous water. There was a narrow shaft through which light filtered in, but here, instead of piercing the gloom like a thrusting blade, it merged with the sea, became diffused and impregnated the whole pocket of water, bathing every hole and corner in gentle, liquid brightness that had no shadows.

And the place was teeming with life: anemones, sea urchins, and other treasures that the benevolent sea is continually renewing. Like a new Siegfried armed with magic hood, I braved the people of the shadows. Holding with one hand to the base of white sea-fan, I thrust my arm into a narrow niche. No, what a shame! Our horrible friend was no longer there.

A year ago that treasure cave had had its guardian, a horrible ogre, a grotesque and simple dwarf, Alberich, in reality a little shy octopus, which we, uncertain of its sex, called Suzy. Suzy was quite fond of Alan and me. With George she remained very reserved, huddled at the back of her crack, tentacles stuck to the rock, yet the mere sight of Philip was enough to send her into a fury. Gesticulating frantically, her terror veiled behind a show of aggressiveness, she would spread around her a generous protective cloud of ink. Philip was quite hurt at the way he was ostracized.

One afternoon at the beginning of September Alan came up from the cave, his face red.

"Come and see what Suzy's doing. There's another octopus with her."

To see what Suzy was doing we went down in turn using the pump apparatus. Philip wanted to go too, but we would not let him, feeling that at a moment of such gravity and so serious in its consequences Suzy ought to be spared all other emotion.

There was no doubt what was happening: hanging from the rock the two octopuses were clasping each other in a long viscous embrace, while one of the newcomer's tentacles was thrust in under the pimply fold of Suzy's "mantle". The situation remained unchanged until supper time, when Claud, whose turn below it had been, reported that Suzy, gripping the rock with only two tentacles, had freed herself from the embrace, then had somehow got on top of her exhausted husband, clasped him in her six remaining tentacles, and was now slowly eating him alive.

I went down a second time at eight o'clock and by then all that remained of the male octopus was a motionless, dull eye, and eight arms hanging limp, and pale. Slowly Suzy was enveloping her victim, hauling him in. Now and again first one, then another of her tentacles would release its suction, describe a flourish in the water as it stretched out to its maximum, then fold in again, grope for a moment and with empty suckers fasten on once more, only a little lower down on the bag of grey skin. Then, all together, the long muscular arms would swell and retract, raising the victim a fraction of an inch. Suddenly I realized that the body of the unfortunate husband had almost disappeared; its eye was engulfed in the gritty membrane that joins the tentacles to the body.

The arms alone still hung down, paralyzed and useless, and the whole looked like one monstrous octopus with sixteen arms instead of eight.

Suzy was taking her time. When I stretched out my hand towards her, she gave me a look that was slightly anxious, yet still trusting and almost conspiratorial. I was obviously meant to understand that that was not the moment to try to play.

The pocket dilated, greedy little quivers passed through it, and two tentacles fluttered, then curved inward to meet under the body of the male and enfold it once and for all. Suzy was then very like a cherub, chubby-cheeked, and ingenuous.

When George returned from his visit below he quoted one of the fathers of the Church.

"According to St. Thomas", he said, "love is an appetite for oneness. . . ."

That last summer's camp had provided us with everything, even a romantic fight with a large devil-fish at the mouth of the great breach in *Makassar's* side. But don't worry. Forget Gilliatt and the adventures of *Nautilus*. Philip was in no danger. In fact such an encounter was no more hazardous, or repugnant, than coming across a bat in a belfry. Even so, Philip confessed that he had shuddered when, with "Felix the Cat" strapped on his back, he felt the sticky brute take hold of him and saw its tentacles with their whitish suckers enlarged and ready, unfolding and twining in the shadows. Resigned to the fact that he would never be able to charm an octopus, and perhaps secretly glad of being able to get his own back, Philip pulled out his knife and thrust it into the horrible pimply skin between the two yellow eyes. Soon the suction was released and Suzy's sister no more than a whitish limp pocket animated by intermittent, ineffectual convulsions.

The goddess lying in her packing-case in the gloom had other and better guardians in the corners and sharp edges of the torn plates on which we could have caught, and in the physiological accidents that could have resulted from not paying proper attention to Haldane's tables.

The worst experience was not Philip's, but Claud's. He had gone in through the breach with our autonomous equipment, then lost his sense of direction in the huge belly of the wreck and been unable to find the breach again. In the darkness which was almost complete, he had banged into the walls of the hold, bounced off on to steel plates covered with sticky creatures that retracted beneath his touch or made off in sinuous silent flight, and all the while he had the haunting knowledge that each breath lessened his reserve of air, made the pointer on the gauge he could not see creep back a little more, that soon perhaps the pointer would be at nought, breathing become difficult and the supply of air give out.

Claud hates to talk of that adventure, and it takes a lot of persuasion before he will—and he won't if he is due to be diving soon. "What made me panic most was the gurgling of my bubbles, for it reverberated most oddly, like in a church. In the end my eyes must have got accustomed to the darkness, for I was able to make out a vague glow in front of me and below. I got out by swimming on my side like a limanda, in such a funk that I almost passed out. I went straight up to the surface."

He stopped, then ended in altogether too matter-of-fact a tone:

"But I needn't have worried. It wasn't till I was half-way up that I thought of looking at the pressure gauge, and there was still forty pounds."

*   *   *

All that, however, brought us no nearer the golden goddess with the emerald eyes. Having proved that the first breach did not provide a convenient route to No. 3 hold, we decided to concentrate our efforts on the second breach. Judging by the plan, this seemed better placed, but unfortunately it was rather badly blocked. If we could use it, there seemed little doubt that we would not have far to go in the belly of the wreck to reach the level of the treasure we sought.

Our supply of compressed air was giving out. Naturally we used the recharging bottles always in the same order: the first to refill, the other two in succession to bring up the pressure. By the end of September however we were going down with a pressure of only 150 lb. Our cylinders each had a capacity of four litres and thus theoretically the limit of our stay at a depth of 130 feet was five minutes. It was however even less than this because we were using an axe to try and remove some of the debris blocking our way, an exhausting job that considerably increased our consumption of air; and also, we had to leave ourselves a slight margin.

We stuffed ourselves with ephedrine so that we could get down quickly to the depth at which we worked without being troubled by pains in the ears. Hanging on to the side of the boat with one hand we would hold the mouthpiece out of the water in the other and only cram it into our mouths at the last moment, just before we dived. George had the idea of measuring the length of the dive by releasing an electric light bulb the moment he arrived at the bottom. We counted one minute twelve seconds from the moment his frogmen's feet disappeared till the bulb emerged.

Thus each time we went down our time was slightly less, and before long we were saying that each dive was going to be the last. Then having got up again safely, one of us was sure to say:

"One more?"

"O.K. One more."

And we would brandish our thumbs in the air with a stupid smile. It was, of course, becoming more and more problematical whether we could succeed. Knowing George as we did, we also realized that he would only give up when one of us had got stuck without air at the bottom. The prospect was not pleasant, for "Felix the Cat" did not incorporate a reserve device, nor was there a weighted belt that could be jettisoned, while by itself Felix was too heavy and difficult to haul right up to the surface. Thus, each time we went down, with less air than the last time, we wondered whether we would be the one to whom it would happen. Our state of mind was comparable to that of a group of soldiers advancing across ground that was mined and every now and again changing the person in the lead.

We dived in the following order: Claud, Philip, myself, George. Alan was excluded as he would have wasted air to no purpose. Claud and Philip dived on Saturday evening. I saw how pleased Claud was when he emerged just at the last moment with both cylinders empty, and the queer expression on Philip's face—he was the next to go down—as he watched the cylinders being recharged, which again left them with a pressure slightly less than the time before.

I was horribly nervous all the time Philip was down. My legs were leaden with apprehension. Naturally, I could have told George that I was crying off, but he would just have gone down instead, so it was not really possible. Seated in the stern, I watched the patch of Philip's bubbles: perhaps they would come to a sudden stop. I tried to tell myself that I was anxious for Philip's sake, but it was not that at all. It suddenly came to me that, on the contrary, I was hoping for an accident, anything that would save me from having to go down after Philip with apparatus that was all but empty. I reproached myself bitterly for this nasty, treacherous feeling, and, to try and make up for it I prayed that nothing should happen to him. That seemed to work, for within less than two minutes Philip was clambering back into the boat, the gauge at nought, as pleased with himself as someone who has escaped the hangman's noose. Politely he handed me the dripping apparatus.

"The pleasure is yours!"

We recharged the cylinders at once, and this time the pointer did not get higher than eighty. Idiotically I tapped the glass to see if it would not go up any farther. On the contrary, as the cylinders became colder, the pointer dropped slightly. I was in a hurry to get it over. I thought the relieved look on the faces of Claud and Philip quite indecent. They, of course, were well out of it, for, whatever happened, there would not be enough air for another series. They were kindness itself.

"Here's your mask. I've swilled it out for you. What flippers would you like?"

"What; the straps? I'll tighten them a bit for you."

"No go," said George. "It's too late in the evening. You can dive to-morrow afternoon, Francis. And I'll go after you. Alan can take the opportunity and go down to sixty feet with the pump apparatus to make sure that the rope is still fast on the mast and there's no risk of the buoy floating off."

*   *   *

I could not get to sleep that evening. There was an east wind and gusts kept shaking the tent, while gulls dived down on our shelter crying like lost souls. Beside me Alan was twisting and turning, jerking every now and again like a dog when it dreams. Poor Alan! His sleep seemed to be troubled by fear of the morrow. A dive down to the masts, some eighty feet perhaps, was not so very dreadful. Would we ever manage to change Alan? I was beginning to wonder whether we would ever turn him into a V.C., whether he would not always remain the timid little boy at his mother's apron-strings, brave only when it came to cupping-glasses, poultices, injections and spoonfuls of cod liver oil. If his father had lived, no doubt he would have been brought up very differently, and I could not help regretting the Alan that might have been.

Some time after midnight the wind dropped abruptly, but I still could not sleep. Lying on my back, as stiff as a corpse, I no longer thought of Alan, but of myself and my fear. I was no longer aware of my body; it was as though all that was me was concentrated in my head, and that was crowded with confused thoughts.

If anything were to happen to me, it would be no more than just retribution for my horrible wish while Philip was diving. Fortunately, the next day would be Sunday. Being after midnight, it was Sunday already, the fifteenth Sunday after Whitsun. We would read Mass, and in honour of the day we would not have smoked herrings for lunch. Then a siesta till three o'clock and off we would go, heading north-east towards our discreet little buoy. Alan and I would be wearing pea-jackets over our trunks and would only need to strap on the apparatus, and our hearts would be racing slightly.

*   *   *

It was about half-past three when the cork triangle came into sight.

176

Securing a rope to a wreck: it will guide other swimmers down

Left: Using a water-proofed compass for under sea navigation

Right: When we reached the wreck we disturbed myriads of little fish

Right: At the wheel of a sunken ship

Left: Beneath the bridge of the *Macassar*

Left: We sometimes swim through shoals of fish

Right: Frogmen exploring anti-submarine defence netting

"Get ready," said George.

It was quite fresh and Alan and I shivered as we took off our pea-jackets. Claud checked the apparatus. I staggered when the boat rolled as I was putting on the heavy cylinders and had to hold on to the gunwale. "Bad omen," I said to myself stupidly. Then I tried to console myself with the thought that, there being so little air, my ordeal would be of short duration. Alan went in first, with his usual grimaces.

*　　*　　*

With the axe at my belt I nose-dived into the blue, passing Alan who was going down a yard at a time clinging to the rope that he was to see securely tied fifteen fathoms lower down. There were the masts, the ruined bridge. With great scissor movements of my legs, and helped by the weight of the apparatus, I sped on at full speed. Slight pain in my left ear; compensation of the lungs under the pressure that was doubling, trebling, quadrupling. Deep breaths and almost no exhalation. Then there was the sand and I flattened out and sped on for the breach. Nobody, not even George, could have got down more quickly and used less air.

Then I was at the breach and plying the axe on the hard debris. Furious though my attack was I had to regulate my breathing: one . . . two . . . one . . . two . . . every seven seconds a bubble of crystal detached itself from the nape of my neck and burst against the torn plates and sharp corners of the overhanging hull. I stirred up a cloud of mud in the calm water, so that when I looked down I could not properly see the pointer of the pressure gauge on my stomach at the level of my trunks.

I was not afraid when I felt inhalation becoming difficult and the air giving out in the mouthpiece. A stoppage at

130 feet was nothing very serious. I did not even let go of the axe. I withdrew, swimming on my back, and once beyond the overhang sent myself up towards the surface with great thrusts of my flippered feet. But, at 100 feet, level with the bridge, I began to panic. Fatigue was making my limbs heavy. I dropped the axe, the weight of which was braking my ascent. With the reduced pressure the valve let a little fresh air through, but suddenly my head began to swim. I could see the rope bending and dancing through the haze. Perhaps Alan was clinging there. If only I could see him. But no, I was all alone. My body was letting me down. I had every reason to be afraid. Was I going to faint? Whatever I did, I must not let go of the mouthpiece. I must clench my teeth on the rubber. My hand clutched the chromium-plated branch-tube. Up, up. Just a few more thrusts with my flippers.

Everything was shifting, swaying, tilting, and everywhere were bubbles, in clusters, in swaying columns, all air that had come from my body. I was suffocating. I had a great lump in my throat. It was pretty certain now that I was going to faint before I could get back to the surface and the light. If I had had a weighted belt I would have undone it. But I didn't have a belt at all. The sea would take hold of me and take me slowly down again, like a dead sailor weighted with shot.

I could see a lot of royal blue, swirling bubbles and fireworks. Clench your teeth, I told myself. Don't let go of the mouthpiece, that is life, bite on to it as long as you can. In a few minutes the last of the bubbles will have vanished and you will be on your back somewhere near the bottom.

But I did not want to die. Sixty feet above me was the boat dancing on the surface. I could see its black keel. It was like a captive balloon and in it were Alan, Claud, Philip and George, waiting for me.

Dear God, take me up there. It is so close.

My legs were inert, but I still had my arms. I should be able to heave myself up, even with all that ironmongery on me.

No air at all now. Everything was becoming blurred. The universe was tottering. There was an explosion of stars. I felt a briny taste in my mouth and dropped into blackness.

*   *   *

I was in the bottom of the boat. George's hands were on my chest and as he kneaded my sides I could hear his voice like a dull buzz coming from very far away. I could make out shapes, but not yet see colours, everything appeared silhouetted, either grey or black.

"He's opened his eyes", George said.

I shut them again, for I was very tired and had no desire to have to answer questions. When I opened them again the world had reverted to normal: George's shorts were white, his sweater blue. Philip's scarf was red. The boat had got broadside on and was rolling heavily. All at once I remembered. I felt very weak, but perfectly lucid. I wanted to know how long I had remained in the water. Perhaps I risked having another accident from decompression. The main thing, though, was to be back in the boat.

The rolling stopped. Philip and Claud had started the motor, we were going back. Spray was showering in. George spread a bit of sail-cloth over me, smiled and jerked his thumb upwards. I was sure it was he who had fished me out. Under the sail-cloth I could not brandish my thumb, but I smiled back. For some minutes I kept an eye on myself, afraid that I might suddenly feel a sharp pain that would mean the formation of a bubble of nitrogen somewhere in my tissues. But no, nothing happened. Only I had an appalling headache.

* * *

We doubled the point of the cove and altered course. George bent over me:

"Good old Francis! You know it was Alan fished you out?"

"Alan? From the bottom?"

"Yes, indeed. From 130, right at the bottom. He was coming up from his dive with the kamikaze when your bubbles stopped. He did not even come out, but went straight down again.

As I swallowed a couple of aspirins I could imagine the scene behind George's words: Alan, just about to hoist himself back into the boat, when the patch of bubbles was suddenly no longer there. A glance at a watch. The decision to be taken in a matter of seconds: whether to loose five vital minutes unharnessing Alan and putting the equipment on one of the others, or risk everything and send Alan down, despite his fifteen years, his funk, and everything.

"We followed him on the gauge", said Philip. "He went down like a stone, enough to burst his ear-drums. He found you very quickly. You were on your back, ten yards from the side of the wreck, with the mask in place and the comforter in your mouth. He tied a rope under your arms, then gave a number of tugs to tell us that we could haul you up . . ."

I turned my head and looked at Alan. He was sitting in the bows and said nothing. Despite the sweaters and rugs in which George had wrapped him, he was still shivering with cold. He seemed to be still searching inside and had the same expression of wincing at some internal battle, that was both moving and irritating.

"To go down to 130 feet in the kamikaze", exclaimed Claud admiringly. "You must have been breathing pure carbon dioxide. What did it feel like?"

"That deserves a celebration", Philip put in.

I murmured:

"Thanks, Alan, thanks."

He was beginning to feel a bit warmer and was not trembling quite so violently. I thought that the demon of his fear must be exorcised for ever. It would return, no doubt, but it would never be his master again.

George was silent; then, turning to Philip he said:

"Go forward, Philip, and see that the painters are ready." And then almost in the same tone:

"Let us thank God."

There was a silence. Then George turned towards Alan and in a voice that was suddenly shaky, he said softly:

"I think your father must be very proud of you now."

*   *   *

That evening, after supper, no one proposed that we should try one more dive. We had to give up. There was only eight, eighteen and eighty pounds respectively left in our three cylinders, and, of course, nothing in "Felix the Cat". Sitting beside the camp fire that we lit each night, George unfolded the plan of *Makassar* for the last time. We had nothing with which to reproach ourselves. What needed to be done called for explosives and other equipment, especially much better supplies of compressed air, and perhaps even a special blow-pipe for oxy-acetylene cutting. In order to prove that we had located and reached the wreck, we would go down the next morning with Felix to get one of the letters of corroded copper that still spelled the name on the stern, and this we would take back to V. as evidence of semi-success. We had done all we could for the time being. Unfortunately! Next year we would start again with better equipment.

George let go of one end, and the plan of *Makassar* rolled up on its own. We were all feeling rather sad.

Philip jerked back his head.

"I wonder if Suzy'll have her babies before we go", he said, and we burst out laughing.

"At any rate", George said, "that will give us a chance to come back next year to force the last few yards." For a moment he hesitated, then he added: "The best thing would be if we could keep getting closer to the statue without ever reaching it. That would be perpetual victory . . ."

*   *   *

After prayers George and I were, as always, the last to leave the fire.

Muscles relaxed, wrapped in a down sleeping-bag, I felt filled with happiness. I thought how without Alan I could easily have been elsewhere at that moment, lying beside the wreck or stiff and cold in the tent, dead. I had had the same thought about George a fortnight before, but when it concerned myself the idea did not worry me.

That evening, George was the one who was upset.

He asked me to forgive him and I told him not to be an idiot. After that neither of us said anything for a while. I felt George's eyes on me. It was my turn to have a mysterious aura, and he was looking at me, as I had been looking at him. I waited for him to speak.

"Tell me", he said, "when you felt that it was all up?"

His voice trembled with the importance of the question. I thought a moment before replying.

"Well," I said, "from the moment I thought I was done for . . ."

George was no longer looking at me. The flames of the fire were dancing in his eyes. I can still see him, tilted back and rocking slightly, one bare knee held in the ring of his clasped hands.

"George, all the time I was at the bottom until I recovered consciousness in the boat there was nothing at all, no light, exactly like very deep sleep without dreams. Everything black. George, do you think that that can be what death is?"

I believe there must have been a sort of terror in my voice.

George stopped rocking, let go of his knee and stretched out his long legs, while he thought.

"That doesn't prove anything, Francis", he said at length. "You were not properly dead. The soul must leave afterwards, you see? And pass . . . through a sort of black tunnel before it emerges into the light and is finally freed. You did not go quite to the end of the tunnel; then you came back . . ."

"One ought to be able to go right to the end and then come back", I said.

"If you went right to the end, then you would see God", said George, "and do you think anyone would want to go back after that?"

*   *   *

George insisted that I should go down again as soon as possible. He was afraid that my accident might have left me with an instinctive horror of it, and I too was afraid of being afraid, but when the water covered me, when the foaming waves closed over me, I realized that I bore our

Marvellous Kingdom no grudge, that I belonged to it just as much as ever.

When I emerged, George asked with a hint of anxiety in his voice: "All right?"

With both hands on the gunwale and the waves slapping at me I could not put up a thumb, so I gave him a wink instead.

"I would like to go down again", I said.

"No you don't", said George. "That's enough. It's my turn now".

*   *   *

We were returning, laden with our equipment, by the road that runs alongside the sea. We were commenting on the latest visions we had seen.

"A poulpe like that, the biggest I've ever seen."

"A poulpe or a devil-fish?"

"Sorry, but I didn't count the suckers. Did you notice those red sponges on the north wall? Just like calves' liver."

We were still being spattered by the waves breaking on the rocks at our feet.

"If this keeps on, we shan't be able to leave the day after to-morrow."

The prospect was not one to sadden us.

"All the better. It won't be our fault."

"We've never yet dived in such a sea. I lost sight of your bubbles almost at the start, as soon as you reached the level where they break up. There wasn't a sign of them."

We were shivering and dripping.

"If the Scout Master could see us!"

"He would be quite right. It's quite ridiculous to dive in such weather. I've noticed that the longer we go on, the greater idiots we become; it's as though we always had to go one better. We never learn."

"I sometimes wonder", George, who was walking beside me went on, "why it is we do this. It's not for the statue now. There's no material reason. If anyone told us to do it, we wouldn't. We are wrong to do it and we know that, yet we do it all the same."

"The sea", I ventured.

"Oh no. I know that we love the sea more than anything and that is why we have chosen this form of adventure; but suppose we did not love the sea or that the sea was forbidden to us, do you think we would give up adventure because of that? Of course not. We would take to parachuting or flying."

"It's the adventure we love."

"Exactly, and the question is: why? Our Scout Master Maurice is perhaps right when he says that we are only looking for 'a personal satisfaction'. And when he's in form, he even adds, 'vainglorious and morbid' . . ."

The wind dropped suddenly as we came behind a spur of rock, and peace surrounded us, strange after the cold and stinging gusts. I could hear the sobbing of the spring near the grave of the sailor from *Galathea*, and I gave a little laugh in which there was no gaiety. The exultation of battling had left me and I felt weary and my thoughts confused. I thought of my accident again, of fainting and falling into blackness.

"We are neither saints nor heroes", I said. "We are adventurers."

George stopped, put down the heavy pump and seized me by the shoulders. His face was close to mine and I was struck by the almost ascetic thinness of it. The little scar on his cheek was glowing. Although fixed on me, his eyes did not seem to be seeing me, but some other more distant reality beyond my body.

"We are adventurers, but you have decided too easily,

Francis. I would like to be a saint or a hero as well, and not just an adventurer. I don't want us to be mere adventurers."

He hesitated a moment, then lowered his voice and added:

"Especially you . . ."

It is true, the splendours were a mere pretext, and we would have dived into water that was dull, dead and empty merely to savour the act of departing from the world, for the mere pleasure of feeling the sea close over us.

And that we should always want to go one better was quite legitimate, for courage engenders habit and habit kills fear. And what would become of courage without fear? It would become like a shell and we the hermit crab. That is why I believe that one must always go a little beyond the limit of what one is accustomed to do, of one's training, and to venture as far as the unexplored where one can still find cold, surprise and fear.

20

SINCE coming to the island we have done as we did last
summer, and always got up at dawn to take advantage
of the calm sea at that hour; but this morning, after our
dives last night, have slept badly. The canvas of the tent
is golden with sunshine and on it some little spiders are
dashing about like frantic silhouettes. George and the
others are still asleep. I can hear their regular breathing,
the life-giving breaths that suddenly and miraculously
become visible and bright under water.

Before going on with my account of the events of last
year, let me tell what happened just a few hours ago while
it is still fresh in my mind and my nerves are still quivering, a proof that nothing has changed and that we are
still always trying to go one better, as George said last
year.

Yesterday, about eleven o'clock in the evening, we
went back to the sea. We walked along the shore, apparatus
on our backs, masks and frogmen's feet in our hands. On
our right and almost at our feet was the sea with little
frothy waves that were pale silver in the light of the moon.
We passed the black mass of *Sagitta* lying beached at the
end of a tackle and finally came to the other side of the
beach, and the litter of rocks at the foot of the cliff that
continues vertically for another sixty-five feet under the
water, even with a slight overhang. We were strangely
silent as we put on our frogmen's feet, opened the taps on
the cylinders and tested the commutators of our long
aluminium watertight torches that we fixed on to our left
forearms in such a way that we could direct the beam and

187

still have our hands free. Four powerful beams were already intersecting or playing about the choppy black water into which we were going to descend. The fifth torch, which was Claud's, lit, trembled, went out, came on again, and stayed alight.

Just before he put in his mouthpiece George said in his calm voice:

"I hope we see some congers and morays. Ready?"

"Ready."

The five beams shot skywards to show that we were ready, then turned down again on to the water in a sort of solemn salute as we took to the water. One by one the cones of light shortened and disappeared as the thick glass broke the surface and went in.

The cold embrace of the water quickened our breathing. Overwhelming night closed over us with the sea. The ground dropped away abruptly. What depth were we now. Fifteen feet? Fifty?

Our hands clenched in a sort of panic as the shafts of light from our torches cut into the menacing gloom; yet there was a happy air about it all when the cascades of bubbles were caught for an instant in the dancing beams, and in the gleam and sparkle of fish.

Without any desire for independent action we glided down in a compact group towards the sandy plain that stretched away from the foot of the cliff. There was the bottom. Down we went, like slow motion parachuting. Seventy feet. Invisible particles suspended in the water flattened our beams as though they were striking a wall a yard ahead of us. For an instant I put my hand over my lens and at once the phosphorescence on the sea floor lit up, dimmed and continued to twinkle.

Talk about Captain Nemo and his "Ruhmkorff lamp" under 500 feet of water in the depths of the forests of the

Island of Crespo. It was as though we were there, the darkness having given us another 400 feet of depth. The water pressing on our shoulders seemed ten times as dense as mud; the surface and the sky had withdrawn to the very limits of the possible. To savour such a night you have to go down to depths that man can only reach in a suit of protective steel.

Alan went off to the right along the rock-face, his torch growing smaller and smaller, then vanishing. He was searching for a squill-fish which is supposed to be out and about at that hour. George stood leaning against the rock, shining his torch on it and picking out the minute details of its mosaics, its Japanese gardens, anemones, algae and sponges. Suddenly George's arm halted, the beam of his torch stopped on the fan of a tilted sea-fan. There, asleep on its side, was a *serran écriture* and in the light of our torches we could see the true dark red colour of the Japanese characters that decorated its snout. Tremors passed through it, as the light woke it up. Slowly it turned upright, like a wreck being refloated, then it shot away in a panic and disappeared into the night.

Then a long shrill, guttural cry told us that Alan must have found something. There he was, a bright point of light that grew and grew, until it was close. He beckoned to us to follow and we glided off several yards. What strange phosphorescent fish we were! Alan pointed his torch at the opening of a hole, then slowly withdrew it. Two feelers appeared, then a head with button eyes. It was not a squill-fish, but a heavy one in porcelain armour, a blue lobster. Attracted by the light, it came out with small steps, its two claws in front. It wagged its feelers, either out of anxiety or inquisitiveness. Then seemingly reassured—or disappointed—it returned disdainfully, in backward movement, into its hole.

Above us, a long ribbon detached itself from the rock, brushed us and disappeared. What was it? We, too, were both curious and afraid, and also slightly intoxicated by being there not as man the omnipotent, but as among equals; prey among prey. Vainly we brandished our torches. Their beams could not pierce water to which there was no end, water that absorbed them in a halo of turbid haze out of the centre of which perhaps a muraena would suddenly emerge, nape swollen with cruelty. The light could easily attract one, ought to attract one. But no. There were three little fishes, strictly parallel, and that was all. Which was both a relief and a disappointment.

Instinct prompted Philip to turn his beam in the other direction. Purplish red, half out of its hole, another muraena swayed its head from side to side. What a muscular, supple body! What cruel eyes. The gaping mouth was like a crocodile's, opening and shutting interminably, while the five beams of our torches were on it.

Is that really what George sought? I suspect that it was not the spectacle of congers and muraenas in pursuit of their prey that took him again and again to the bottom of the sea, but something quite different.

We emerged out of the black water, and returned to the camp fire which an armful of dry wood quickly resuscitated. Warmed by the glow and reassured even more by the silent presence of the others, we sat feeling pleasantly secure, all barriers between us gone in the consciousness of what we shared. Our eyes at that moment were soft with the sense of brotherhood such as men used to know when the world was young.

21

I⊤ was the day after we had to give up our attempts to discover valuable things in the wreck of *Makassar* that we saw the big sailing ship. It was a grey, cloudy day, but the sea was calm. Foresail braced to the wind, jib struck, mainsail half braced, she hove-to to the east of our island, about a mile from the wreck. Through our glasses we could see figures busy on the deck, but they could not have seen our camp which was hidden by a spur of rock. A queer sort of instinct had sent us flat on our stomachs behind the bushes. As the glasses passed from one to the other, each pronounced his opinion:

"Perhaps a coaster."

"Or a sponge-fisher."

George gave a nervous laugh.

"As long as she hasn't come to fish for something quite different."

The presence of a boat in those unfrequented waters seemed to George unusual to say the least of it.

"You'll see. They'll hoist sail soon and be off", said Philip reassuringly.

Then Alan exclaimed: "The buoy!"

We had forgotten that. Our cork buoy was dancing on the waves 2,000 yards from the intruder, and any moment someone on board might see it. Luckily I had with me my mask, respirator and frogmen's feet. I undressed as I lay flat, then slipped into the water between the rocks. At first I kept along the shore to avoid being seen, and only struck out for the open when I was abreast of the cliff. From time to time I discreetly popped my head up and looked behind me to get my bearings. It seemed impossible that the men in the sailing ship should not see me, but anything was better than running the risk of their discovering the wreck.

No long time passed before I was able to see the triangle of black cork dancing on the waves; but I still had to swim for some minutes before I could make out the long gentle curve of the rope that ran from it to the unfortunate *Makassar*. I did not have my knife and so, keeping myself just at the surface with a wide movement of my flippered legs, I struggled and struggled with the knot and eventually freed the buoy. I let go of the hempen rope and watched it drop slowly through the haze, in long gentle spirals. Then I towed the buoy away for some minutes and abandoned it where the currents would take care of it and cover up our tracks.

*   *   *

Towards evening the strange craft sent in a boat to fetch water from the spring which is mentioned in the Sailing Directions. It was impossible to keep hidden any longer, and to try would only have made us look suspicious. As it was we could easily pass for under-water hunters with no thought for anything but their prey. And then we were really curious to know just who and what these people were.

The little boat reached the shore. There were three men in it, bearded and bronzed, yet dressed in white. We walked towards them. Their ship was the *San Gennaro* and they were diving for sponges on behalf of some company. We shook hands effusively. Realizing how our own anxiety to hide our fears made us exaggeratedly friendly, I could not help wondering whether the Italian

"Once equipped with modern apparatus we penetrated without fear, risk or difficulty into the intimacy of the wreck as often as we liked. We regretted we had not been so equipped two years before"

Above: Floating lightly over the rail of a sunken ship

Above: Testing the strength of weed-encrusted rope and in imagination sounding seven bells

Right: Peering through a hatchway

Left: When exploring underground in the Hole of Hell the water was bitterly cold; the low rock roof necessitated use of a sponge-rubber helmet and an inflated inner tube which was worn round the neck for additional protection

Below: Preparing for exploration underground

sailors' vigorous handshakes did not disguise similar suspicions about us.

"We under-water hunters", Philip kept repeating, while he brandished our one and only under-water gun. "We under-water hunters."

As they passed the grave of the sailor from *Galathea* the Italians removed their caps, then at the spring they filled their large water-skins and an iron drum and went back to the ship which had already lit her riding-lights.

* * *

That night we took it in turn to keep watch on the intruder. As she slowly swung on her anchor, she showed us alternately one, then two white lights. No shadow appeared on the deserted bridge.

Our provisions were almost finished and in two days time we would have to go back to the mainland. Before we left, George wanted to be quite sure about the *San Gennaro*, so the next morning he, Alan and I got into the dinghy and pulled for the Italian ship. A slight swell was crumbling against the squat stern that was painted a dazzling white. Nimbly George went up the ladder and we followed.

A tall swarthy man, his face outlined by a thin rim of black beard was already advancing to meet us. We each introduced ourselves and shook hands with the utmost cordiality. He was Captain Ferrero, from Genoa. The first thing that caught our eye was the wicker case of a Pirelli *"autorespiratore sportivo"*. It was standing by the deck-house and bore the firm's slogan *"Pirelli per il mare"*. The captain must have seen the looks we exchanged, for he lifted the lid and began showing us the rubber bag and the great *bombola d'ossigeno*, the round mask surmounted by a respirator.

"Per le spugne e la caccia subacquea."

George nudged me. It was a sporting edition of the combat apparatus we had been using a year previously. A pity that Philip and Claud were not with us. It conjured up memories of fainting and rinsing mouths with vinegar. Well-made and well-designed though this new model was, the sight of it comforted us. If that was all the Italians had, that is, if they had nothing but closed-circuit apparatus, they could never even dream of going down to the level of the wreck, 130 feet below. To have breathed oxygen under such pressure would have been equivalent to suicide. George was smiling again. Perhaps they really were fishing for sponges.

We were ushered into a minute mess, clean and neat, and regaled from a bottle of chianti in its traditional raffia cage.

As the chianti ran into my glass and Captain Ferrero talked my misgivings came to life again, but I liked the man.

"Alla vostra salute!"

"Your health!"

The Captain seemed to me to be pumping us: so we were fishing: was the water clear round about here, along by the cliffs? How long had we been there? Had we had bad weather? Had we caught a lot?

"In moderation, not so bad".

Then George began asking questions in his turn: had they had good luck, brought up a lot of sponges?

"Discrétamente, discrétamente."

George and the Captain both laughed, the laugh of people who understood each other, and I felt that now nobody was being taken in. All hypocrisy gone, our dialogue was merely a convenient and polite way of disguising competition that was otherwise fierce.

"*Alla vostra salute!*"

"Your health!"

We might almost have added, "And let the best man win."

Questions of interest and ideal apart, we felt that we belonged to the same race as Captain Ferrero with his black beard and blue eyes. We could just as easily have been in his boat and he in ours, while it was quite impossible to imagine someone like our Scout Master Maurice searching with us for a wreck under 130 feet of water. There was no doubt we would play the game where Ferrero was concerned. One is always much closer to one's immediate adversary than to those who have not even been able to learn the rules of the game.

Captain Ferrero seemed to feel very much the same thing about us. There was a conspiratorial light in his blue eyes. We had only known him a few minutes, yet already he seemed an old friend. He came from a different port and sailed under a different flag, yet our paths had converged; not on the surface, but 130 feet beneath in the centre of all that rusted iron that was the reason why we both were there.

As we were no longer in a position to do anything to stop Captain Ferrero, we could sit back and enjoy his wine. We liked the man, and, to some extent, his hospitality.

As we stood saying good-bye to Captain Ferrero on the bridge our eyes went fo'r'ard, between the windlass and the boom. George clutched at my arm. There, beneath a cover which left visible only the two big wheels with their handles, was a powerful four-cylinder pump, one of those used to feed a diver in a proper suit and copper helmet at depths of 200 feet.

There was no longer any possible doubt.

*   *   *

The next day we decided to leave. We went for a last walk across our island, deposited an armful of seafans instead of a wreath on the grave of the sailor from *Galathea*, and pushed off. We saw the *San Gennaro* on the opposite tack which would bring her back to the moorings we had just abandoned. I recognized the white figure of Captain Ferrero; he waved his cap as we passed, and we too waved with a friendliness we really felt, even though we equally sincerely hoped that a squall would drive *San Gennaro* with her big four-cylinder pump aground.

At dawn we re-entered French territorial waters. We felt more and more melancholy as we drew near to the port. To counter the immediate future we had our memories and our plans for the following year.

"You remember that big stone-bass, and Suzy. Next year we'll take provisions for the whole summer . . ."

We were coming back from a world altogether too wonderful for us to be able to envisage returning to the dreary world with which man is content with anything but sorrow. We had escaped from our prison, and yet here we were having to go back to it.

We shut off the motor; the water slid along the sides all too quickly. Regretfully we stroked our yellow, salt-encrusted oil-skins, and thought that soon we must exchange them for jacket and overcoat. Astern to starboard was the interminable beach with its bathers and background of casinos and dance-halls. George looked at it through the glasses and laughed:

"Look at them swarming there, on the very boundary of sea and land, like crabs in a pot. They try to go forward, splash about, flounder, enjoy the feel of water on their skins without knowing why; yet they won't go far: they are cold, they are afraid, so back to the land they take themselves with their petty slyness, petty ambitions, petty ways of living. Ugh!"

22

THIS evening, as we lay rolled in our blankets round the camp fire, George paced up and down lecturing us on the subject of our aspirations and efforts. I rather suspect that a certain amount of paradox has crept into George's theories, but of course paradox can be one way of arriving at certain truths. Anyway it was all very picturesque, and rather fascinating.

The turn of the century, the development of machines, growth of the towns and, as a sort of reaction, the flight of a whole generation of youth to nature, silence and solitude: the Wandervogel with their guitars and leather trousers, the pioneers, the first Scouts . . . the Scout movement was then something original where boys were concerned: Red Indianism, the bush, the camp, the mystery of the road, all according to one's age. Now these elements of originality have all but disappeared. Everybody goes camping, everybody pretends to be seeking to regain contact with nature which thus ceases to be nature. Among the large numbers of bare-headed youth in shorts, the Scouts are no longer pioneers, not even guides, but companions. The poor Scouts have had everything taken from them, even their songs. All the better really, for imitation is the surest sign of success. But that can't happen without a certain degradation.

Before, there had been the "Camp", a word that carried prestige. Now there was only camping, and that also conjured up pictures, such as Aunt Ursula camping, of Uncle Ernest buying a portable cooker for camping, an inflatable mattress for camping!

Last Easter holidays we conquered a dream territory that none is likely to dispute our possession of very quickly! It was not an adventure that redounds to my credit, for I took part in it under constraint and against my inclination, but it was an adventure which made our most daring dives seem poor by comparison.

In February George fell in love with the idea of speleology. I realized that to him this did not mean clambering about in clay or going down hundreds of feet dangling at the end of a rope. George did not become interested till you got to the problem of negotiating syphons or the study of resurgence. He gave us quite a little lecture on "the primordial scientific interest of spelæan exploration", the study of the insects in caves, our "contemporary ancestors", "living fossils" miraculously preserved from normal evolution by the constancy of their milieu. In this respect only spelaean fauna was of comparable interest.

There then followed a long dissertation on the theory of archaic characteristics and adaptive characteristics imposed on spelaean animals by the dynamism of their milieu (cecity, elongation of the antennae, depigmentation, etc.), and, in conclusion, George assured us that by comparing the animals found in the caves of various continents one could get an idea of the ancient continental links and even classify them chronologically by the extent of the adaptive characteristics.

There was little doubt, according to George, that we would be able to contribute our mite, etc.

Naturally, I was not taken in. These continental links were just eye-wash, like the habits of the hermit-crab and holothurian secretions; what attracted George was the darkness, the blind fish, the limpid, icy waters constricted in tunnels of bare, shiny rock. Personally I had very little to say. The same feelings that prevented me going inside wrecks made me shrink from the idea of subterranean rivers without surface, roofed in with rock, and far from any direct contact with the sun and the air; and I could only too easily see us bumping against the ceilings of submerged corridors and unable to get back through the labyrinth to the narrow hole that would lead out into free water and then to the air.

However, to the Pyrenees we went and on the little steep roads we rediscovered some of our underwater solitude.

Let me here give thanks to the Abbé A. of Saint-Pé, experienced speleologist, whose help in the circumstances was so precious to us.

After some fierce discussion we had decided to use the kamikaze, our apparatus for air-tube and pump. Claud, who was a great protagonist of "Felix the Cat", was sure that only autonomous equipment would allow us to explore efficiently and safely, for a feed tube could not help getting pinched in the rock. In support of his argument he quoted Commandant Cousteau's account of his expedition to Font-Estramar, where thanks to Cousteau's equipment considerable depths were reached. George's objection was that it would be impossible for us in the Pyrenees to recharge our cylinders quickly and that would put an intolerable limitation on the number of dives we could make. Besides that, "Felix the Cat" having been constructed in haste had a pressure-valve that stuck up too much from the cylinders which were themselves cumbersome; the valve was also placed so that it projected outwards, and any sudden jolt could easily result in the high-pressure tube breaking. The kamikaze on the other hand had the advantage of taking up much less space. A priori, to squeeze one's way about it, would be better to have ventral rather than dorsal equipment; when negotiating a particularly narrow place the diver could always compress the bag for some seconds as he, George, had done the preceding summer under the wreck. There was obviously a risk that the long tube would catch or be cut, but the flexone-nylon tube which we had been the first to use for diving was indubitably stout and had undergone the worst of treatment without deteriorating or breaking, as the last few camps had proved. What was more, if we should get into a labyrinth, it would act as an Ariadne's thread.

George's point of view was the one we accepted, though "Felix the Cat" was allotted the role of reserve apparatus, to be used in the event of the diver in the kamikaze requiring assistance in the gloom of his submerged corridor.

*   *   *

When we reached the edge of the hole at the back of the cave, I thought we would all run away, plead that the water was too cold, or pretend that our equipment was not working satisfactorily and so elementary prudence required, etc.

"This is known as the Hole of Hell", Abbé A. said. "I shall tell you some legends about it when we get back up above."

We had certainly no wish to know those legends then.

George laughed rather forcedly and said; "The atmosphere here is certainly sympathetic." Then by the light of the acetylene lamp he began to undress with a slowness that was quite unlike him. Once equipped, respiratory bag on his chest, flippers on his feet, he slid into the hole of limpid water, gasping suddenly as the cold enfolded him.

First, he had to sit down, his head still out of the water, then compressing the respiratory bag, ease himself feet first into a narrow crevice like the mouth of a gutter. The glow of his watertight torch lessened, then suddenly vanished. The feed-tube slid through my hands in little intermittent spurts. Philip and Claud were behind me pumping.

George only just got back. His torch gave too little light as a result of which he tore his respiratory bag on a pointed piece of rock and climbed the last few yards of the steps leading to the air-hole with his mouth full of water. We hauled him out and into the cave more dead than alive; he had cut his calf and blood was pouring down it to the green of his frogman's foot.

"It's tough", he admitted, "but it was the lamp's fault. The apparatus worked perfectly until I tore the bag."

Luckily Claud had brought a spare bag. We decided that we would at once telegraph for a much more powerful torch, and, until it arrived, we would content ourselves prospecting siphons that were not quite so constricted and chaotic.

Don't think, however, that George was in any way put off by his adventure. That very evening, with the promising smile of a guide showing tourists some historical sight, he outlined our programme:

"Well, it's agreed then; in the morning 'the Black Water Hole', in the evening 'the Four Steps', and, as soon as possible, back to the 'Hole of Hell'. . . ."

*　　　*　　　*

After dinner Abbé A. told us some tales, but none that was frightening. One I remember was about a Brother Antoine who was born about a century ago. Rough and crafty, daring and crazy, he was a half-wit at whom the children jeered and who took refuge in the mountains where, all by himself, he would spend day after day combing the woods and thickets in search of holes, rock faults and caves, slipping inside them like a kobold to explore, then carefully disguising the entrances so that he should be alone in enjoying those magnificent, dripping chambers. A poor shepherd came and joined him, however, and after that there were two collectors of subterranean treasures, two to search the mountain that was pitted like a Gruyère cheese. Possessing nothing, they had on their lips the humble, gracious smile of those who are content to appear poor while knowing themselves to be prodigiously rich.

Sometimes, however, pride in their discoveries got the better of them and they let a certain amount out:

"Oh, if we liked, what couldn't we tell you! To the north of the mountain there's a wonderful cave, with a great black lake in the middle of it . . ."

The peasants, however, were not interested in the world of the gnomes and never investigated. Nonetheless the tale spread, told in the long winter evenings and gradually a "wonderful cave" became *the* "Wonderful Cave".

In 1916 the shepherd disappeared while on a lone exploration of the caves of Roy. He never returned and his body has never been found. Brother Antoine died some time later, lips sealed on his secret, and all at once the story of the cave became important. The dead are always right. So there were we, also searching for the Wonderful Cave and we imagined ourselves coming out on the far side of the siphon, breaking the surface of the black lake and discovering high above us, almost beyond reach of the beams of our torches, an immense roof with stalactites and draperies.

23

I HAVE described the beginnings of our subterranean adventure and of our set-back at the Hole of Hell. While waiting for a more powerful torch to come, we methodically explored the "resurgences" of the area under the guidance of Abbé A.

The risks of what we were doing being obvious we each found ourselves both afraid, and afraid of appearing to be afraid; wanting not to risk our lives, yet not wishing to shirk our share of the dangers. While the diving rota was being settled our eyes tended to avoid each other, for another's gaze could easily have been too perceptive. It was a queer feeling of mingled generosity and egoism, of self-sacrifice and instinct of self-preservation, and it made the relations between us even closer and at the same time tense. If it isn't you, it will be me.

I could not help thinking of the *ludi gladiatorii* and of the schools of gladiators mentioned in my history book. I had no difficulty in imagining the atmosphere in those preparatory schools, the friendly meals eaten sitting beside those who were to die by your hand, or you by theirs. Apparently free men chose the dangerous profession, "out of love for gold and notoriety". That, I am sure, is a poor explanation. Judging by our own experience, I believe that those young gladiators exercising themselves in the use of sword, trident and net, must have savoured very different pleasures.

On one occasion we had an audience, a family of tourists consisting of father with a camera bouncing on his fat belly, mother with a folding chair, her work and a novel, two boys dressed exactly alike, whom our apparatus sent into a frenzy of excitement, and a fair-haired little girl in a blue dress who was clutching a rose.

I got myself ready with the resolute, tragic air of someone about to stake his life, while the fat father kept exclaiming admiringly:

"That equipment must have cost a lot; the hell of a lot!"

The little girl said nothing. I gave her my, "hero before the battle" smile, with just enough resignation and fatalism added to be specially moving in the circumstances, then I flung myself into the water with threshing legs. I realized at once how stupid I had been, for the slime rose from the bottom in dense puffs. I should have gone up again and waited for it to clear, but I could not because of the girl.

Shivering but calm, I remained at half depth for some minutes until the current had carried it all away, then in the tunnel I went upstream very slowly keeping on the surface, where my head was level with the roof, dodging roughness in the rock and stalactites that dipped themselves in the water. The roof came lower and lower and in the end touched the surface. I compressed the bag slightly with my left arm, and like a great fish obeying the fluctuations of its swim-bladder, went gently down, lamp first. I advanced along a tunnel filled with black water. To my right and left, on the walls, were some queer whitish sponges. I picked some and slipped them into one of my rubber gloves.

A few more yards and the water was no longer flowing. I let myself rise more or less out of habit, and, ow! My head banged on the rock. I was grateful for my sponge-rubber helmet. I must remember that I was underground. But I had to get on. The sandy bottom began to rise, the roof to drop, the walls to move in. The tunnel was like the finger of a glove, filled with water and thrust into the mountain. For a couple of yards I went backwards, then the corridor widened slightly and I was able to turn. It was only on the return journey that I realized where the water came from. Gingerly raising my head I saw the stream of my bubbles strike the roof and at once disappear, no doubt into tiny fissures.

Already a pale hazy sun was lighting up the black water, and at the end of the tunnel was a perspective of green. I switched off my torch and hurried on along the bottom. Light; grass and sticky pebbles; frisky tadpoles; a crinkled surface, and I was out.

George handed me our traditional mug of hot toddy and we inspected the "sponges".

"Can you tell us which are the archaic characteristics and which the adaptive?" Philip asked with a laugh.

The big-bellied father had his own opinion.

"Those are mushrooms", he said.

I would like to have seen him eat them.

As was our custom we decided to make a second descent as a check. George selected Alan.

Alan was fair and angelic-looking, and as he wore shorts, he seemed even younger than he was. Our audience appeared most surprised when he began to undress. The mother was quite horrified and asked him if his parents knew about this. He solemnly assured her that they did and that without their permission he would never dream of doing it. When he inserted the mouthpiece, the poor mother could stand no more and withdrew, exclaiming: "No, Edward. I cannot watch him!"

*　　*　　*

The new torch arrived and we decided to spend Easter

Sunday exploring the Hole of Hell. We went to early Service and then on to the Hole. I was to go down. As he equipped me George and I conversed calmly and naturally, yet I could feel fear bowing my head, as in a few minutes would the roof of rock.

What did "dying" mean? At the wreck of *Makassar* neither George nor I had gone far enough. The end of the corridor remained a mystery, more mysterious than the tunnel of black water into which I was about to go.

Here! My right hand was shaking and the patch of light from the torch kept leaping about. With an effort of will I brought it to a halt.

"Right? Pump!"

Slowly I slid into the hole. Heavens, how cold it was! The bag inflated well, the duck-billed valve vibrated in unseemly fashion that made the others laugh. Then I had my feet in the fissure. I was slithering in on my back, and was under the surface. The lid of rock closed over me, forcing me to go deeper. I slipped sideways. Already there was a black wall of water behind me. Ahead, in the beam of the torch, my bubbles streamed upward to strike the roof in a multitude of little balls that rolled about until they lodged in the unevennesses, tiny pockets of air that would stay there perhaps for years, little balls of mercury that no human eye would see in that prevailing absolute darkness.

Progress was slow along a slope of thirty degrees. The tubular bathometer recorded twenty feet, but in linear extent I had gone twice as far. The groping beam of my torch rebounded off the rock, lost itself down the axis of the diving tunnel, then suddenly it caught on a protruding block. Was that the end? No, false alarm. You could squeeze past at the side. The respiratory bag was too fat, and I crushed it in with a great eruption of bubbles.

Then, taking very small breaths, I just managed to get past and let the artificial lung inflate again.

There was the candelabra, the projection of rock coming down from the roof that George had told me about. That was where he had stopped last time. To-day, I would go farther. The tunnel began to level out again, the roof lay at an angle of forty-five degrees, the result of some landslide. I swam along with successive small thrusts of my feet, like a fish in a bottle. The rock was bright like marble; no fauna, no flora; nothing. I was the first to see it. The first to reveal those shapes and colours to the light. Of course, they had already existed, but had been invisible, useless, dead and lost beneath their covering of absolute night. Only now, in the light, did they exist properly, were created a second time, as it were, thanks to me.

I kept as high as I could above the fine sand on the bottom of the fault, for I knew that one clumsy touch with a flipper would raise a thick cloud that might make things difficult on the way back.

I also kept a look-out for eddies, for I was afraid of feeling a current suddenly flowing more and more strongly towards a fissure in the bottom, one of those "swallows" into which subterranean rivers suddenly disappear. I was afraid of feeling myself being irresistibly sucked towards a subterranean waterfall, like a butterfly drawn into a fan. But, no. All was silence and the water remained dead and motionless. Like a block of crystal thousands of years old that closed up again when I had passed.

A spur of rock rose up barring the road, a partition dividing the narrow channel. Was this the final obstacle? Yes. It was impossible to pass. Frankly, I was not sorry. Now, there was a very good reason for stopping and going back. Lying on my side by the edge of the rock, first on the right, then on the left, I shone the powerful torch ahead, its beam more concentrated now by refraction: water as far as you could see. The tunnel continued on the same gentle slope. If it did come out under the black lake of the Wonderful Cave it must be very deep. Quickly I set off on my way back, but was suddenly halted by a backward tug. The tube must have caught. Don't panic; and don't pull, whatever you do! It was my fault, of course, I ought to have carried it with me as I went. Back on my tracks I had to go. Yes, that was it. The tube, floating by the roof, had looped round the "candelabra". With the torch in my right hand, I freed the thin tube with my left, slipping it off and pulling it towards the light. Nothing happened. My heart gave a great leap; was the tunnel blocked? Again I retreated, moving myself back with my hands. It was all right. This was the branch. The tube bent away to the right; I had stupidly gone to the left up a short tunnel.

I was back at the hole, squeezing up the respiratory bag flat in readiness to negotiate the narrow gap. Twenty feet above me a diffuse, yellow light bathed the end of the tunnel; that was the reflection from our acetylene lamps in the cave.

Out.

The pumps stopped the moment the mouthpiece slid from my teeth and hung dangling at the end of its rubber ring.

The others waited.

"Well, I've been right to the end . . ."

Up to George now!

"*Suave, mari magno . . .*"

*   *   *

To check my description and give it scientific exactitude

George decided to make another descent into the arena. The beam of his torch swung across the roof with its stalactites and dropped to the narrow resurgence of icy water.

"*Ave Caesar!*"

Our circus was girdled with shale, capped with rock and filled with water under pressure; the sand on its bottom had never known the blemish of a footstep.

Down George went in a splutter of bubbles. Was he a mercenary gladiator, or a young Christian being thrown to the lions? Was it "*Ave Caesar*" or "*In manus tuas Domine*"? If his only trust was in our equipment, then the former.

Past the black rock George took the left-hand tunnel. The nylon tube slid through my fingers. The intermittent sound of gurgling bubbles decreased, then was gone. The tube stopped, slid on, halted again, silence. What was George thinking of? Of God; himself; or, perhaps, nothing. But probably of the obstacles he must negotiate again before he could return to the air and the light of our acetylene lamps?"

There came a gurgling. Yes, this was George coming back. He was all right. Slowly the tube came in again. George would be rising out of the bowels of the earth. He would be swimming with little thrusts of his flippers, the stream of his bubbles waving above him like great silver wings.

The light of his lamp shone out of the darkness of the tunnel and grew until it had spread right across the surface of the hole; his helmet emerged, then the ringed, shining tubes; and his arms were red with cold. George straightened up, spat out his mouthpiece, took off his mask, switched off his waterproof torch.

"It's beautiful", he said. "By Jove, it's beautiful. If

it weren't for the bubbles, you would think you were floating in air. The water's as clear as that.

"But 'Hole of Hell', what a queer name. This being Easter Day, let's rechristen it and call it the submerged cathedral."

*   *   *

We never found Brother Antoine's Wonderful Cave. Nor did we collect any "spelaean animals" to aid our study of continental links, but we were well pleased all the same, for we had gone as far as was possible.

24

T HIS brings me to the events immediately prior to this second camp on our desert island, a camp that might never have taken ₁lace. Now that it is almost over, now that we are sure of being on the right track, I feel more comfortable about conjuring up the memory of that last (and most serious) obstacle that we had to overcome.

V. had given us a cordial reception, but had told us quite distinctly that he did not wish to continue the experiment, especially when we told him of the presence of an Italian ship in the same waters. After all, the addition of fierce competition to the natural obstacles made the undertaking even more hazardous.

*   *   *

At Whitsun we made some money by exploring the bottom of an Alpine lake on behalf of the Electricity Board which wanted to build something there. It was not very amusing, for the water was even colder than in the Hole of Hell, but they looked after us at least. There was a doctor and a nurse, and we had alcohol frictions before we went in.

The advance the Board paid us enabled us to buy our first autonomous G.C.47 outfit, and it was that we used. Naturally we wore foam-rubber suits like those we had used in the caves. These stopped at your wrists and ankles, so we also wore oiled socks under our frogmen's feet and on our hands mittens impregnated with grease.

Those mittens nearly cost Claud his life. I was in the boat following his descent through an under-water glass.

The grey patch of his bubbles had taken a long time to dissipate against the black wall of bare basalt, then suddenly I saw him coming up out of the depths of the blackness at an ominous speed. I could see him coming a long way off, the water was so clear and still. He was thrusting up with great desperate strokes of his flippers and also swimming with his hands to get up quicker. The glass of his mask was upturned towards the light.

When he had been at 130 feet and the pressure gauge had registered 22 lb., Claud had wanted to switch over to his second cylinder, but his fingers, which were stiff with cold in his mittens that themselves were more slippery with grease than the fur of a seal, had been unable to turn the chromium-plated serrated wheel of the tap, which had been closed too tightly at the last filling. He had struggled with it for a few seconds, until his mask was as flat as a gag and he was suffocating; then he made for the distant surface. As he rose and the pressure decreased, the first cylinder which was down to 8 lb. began to release a little more, so he got five or six breaths.

We hauled him into the boat more dead than alive, his rubber mask all spattered with blood. He panted a while, crossed himself and said:

"In my opinion these wheels on the cylinders ought to be replaced with taps of the traditional type with four studs."

*　　*　　*

At the beginning of July a nine-month-old newspaper that came into our hands by sheer chance brought us news of Captain Ferrero.

Dashmond Castle had picked up survivors from *San Gennaro* which had capsized and gone down. They made no secret of the nature of the expedition. Captain Ferrero, less fortunate than Ulysees, had not enjoyed the protection of the goddess Athene and was not among the survivors. They had got the heavy golden statue with emerald eyes from the belly of *Makassar*, but only for it to slide into the depths for the third time. Poseidon had triumphed once again. Now inside *San Gennaro*, and with her captain, the statue of the goddess again lay beneath the sea. Ferrero had tried to get it to the surface, but it had dragged him down.

The paper gave the position of the wreck as approximately fifty miles east of Cape Figari. The charts for those waters showed a depth of over 650 feet. The goddess had gone deeper each time: first 58 feet, then 130, now 650. None would trouble her there. She was Captain Ferrero's for all eternity.

*　　*　　*

It will be long before I forget the next few days after reading that report, our confusion and the inner conflict of our discussions. The sudden disappearance of the material objective of our enterprise forced us to open our eyes to a number of problems and to ask ourselves a certain number of questions about the very motives of what we did. At the beginning we had not thought much about this; but as early as the eve of the trial of our pump apparatus, George had asked himself that question without being able to answer it. Then there had been the business of salvaging the statue, and that gave us the proof of the value of what we were doing as a weapon to counter the doubts of the other half of our minds. Then action came before everything, and we thought it time enough to philosophize when we had attained our objective. Now, in the course of a few seconds we had been bereft of all our arguments and our pretexts were no longer valid. We had to do some thinking. All our doubts, queries, scruples, that we had carefully relegated to the backs of our minds, came flooding back again, demanding to be answered and satisfied, or that we should give it all up.

George had the courage to see this clearly and to put into words the *malaise* that afflicted us all. How far would one call an adventure legitimate when the sole justification for it was the pleasure it afforded our bodies and minds? Did we not always return from the depths with empty hands, like the bronze ephebe fished up from the waters of the bay of Marathon? Could we be content with the pretext of art and knowledge? After all, others, better equipped and much more experienced, were already working along those lines.

It was like standing on the brink of a great gulf. We asked ourselves whether our adventures were not really escapist flights from the world of men and their sordid battles and sufferings devoid of grandeur.

In the depths of winter old Rebufat died. We spent the last two nights watching beside him in the big ward in the hospital to which George's father had had him taken. We had been at sea trying out a new type of watertight suit, and had only heard about his illness when we got back.

He died of exhaustion and loneliness, and his death left us feeling very sad. Some months previously he had had to leave his nice little house down by the harbour and move to one room in the working-class district. It was that which had finally killed him. He still tried to make his models, but his gnarled old fingers were always dropping and breaking them.

By the time we got to the hospital where he was, his mind was already wandering. On Christmas Eve his breathing became difficult as it must have in the old days in his copper helmet when the pump was not being worked fast enough. He muttered words we could not understand; his eyes were turned up and his right hand kept jerking from under the sheets to clutch at nothing.

We remembered all the stories he had told us about *Melpomène* sunk on that rocky bottom, about the master-at-arms, about the sponge-fisher and the Pharaoh's treasure, and also the little cloud he always saw in one corner or other of the sky; a little cloud that was made to mean so many different things.

Within a few minutes the house doctor and the nurses arrived, a huge cylinder of oxygen was pulled right up to the bed and the mask was placed on the old man's face. Once he was breathing pure oxygen his respiration became normal again, his outstretched arm stopped its agitated beckoning and just made a few spasmodic gestures. Darkness was falling on the little green-painted room. His breathing was still peaceful, but becoming shallow. We could scarcely make out the movements of his pale hand, so slight they were, and the mask was just a black shadow at the end of the rubber tube.

The hand was suddenly still. In place of the slight intermittent breathing a continuous hiss was coming from the rubber edge of the mask. When the doctor came back, he switched on the light, turned off the tap on the cylinder, and removed the mask. Old Rebufat was no more. This time he had dived for ever to the heart of our Marvellous Kingdom. He need never return to the surface.

* * *

On 20 May we had a serious accident. Claud was trying out a closed-circuit apparatus of our own manufacture, using superoxygenated air, and at ninety-eight feet he suddenly fainted. George who was escorting him using the Cousteau brought him straight up, but he did not revive till that evening in hospital. We felt ourselves very directly responsible for the accident, for it had originated in a number of errors and things we had neglected. We were shattered.

Then the papers got wind of it. Reporters came swarming round and the thing was written up in the usual style. As a result our poor parents were deluged with letters of condolence, advice or violent criticism, and also with pious exhortations to bring their children up better!

All that had its effect on us, and we could not rid ourselves of the vision of Claud, inert and deathly pale, surrounded by nurses, and not a trace of life in him.

At Cape Brun, Claud had looked dead for only a matter of seconds. On board the *Sagitta*, off our desert island, I had recovered consciousness within a few minutes; but this time death, which we had so long been provoking, seemed to have installed itself for good, and it only withdrew after a difficult struggle in which the issue was long uncertain.

Two years earlier George had said to me one day: "We take ourselves for lords because we sometimes hold life of little account. At our age, that's the least we can do, but is it really enough?" No, it obviously was not enough; but did we even have the right to do it? "Risk" and "adventure" were big words, but did they weigh as heavily as the body of a youth?

And then there was the scene in Claud's room. A real settling of accounts. It was awful. Claud was in bed, lying back with his red head on the bolster. I don't know what set him off, but suddenly there was our meek little Alan with his hands at George's throat, shaking him and trying to throttle him, while George remained unresisting.

"You swine, George, you swine."

George, hands deep in his pockets, his face pale, made no attempt to protect himself.

"You swine! The boats, the sailing, the equipment, that's all you care about. 130 feet. Three cheers for the Sea Scouts. That's all you are capable of; that's all that counts as far as you are concerned. You don't care about us. Look at Claud. If he had died you would no doubt have considered it an 'annoying incident' due to a 'regrettable phenomenon'. You would have put on your best cap and assembled the Troop in full uniform to sing the farewell song. And in the evening you would have asked Francis to play Chopin's funeral march on the piano for our dead hero."

"Shut up, Alan!"

"No, I won't. You're an utter swine, and we're arrant idiots always to follow your lead. And what's it all for? Not for the statue, now that that's gone for good! But just for the swank, just for the few photographs in the papers, for a few bits of coral, a few shells, for nothing at all. Well, haven't you anything to say?"

There was silence. Their two faces were close together, Alan's red and convulsed, George's white and trembling. Suddenly Alan thrust George away so forcefully that his head banged on the wall. It was all over so quickly that neither Philip nor I had time to think of intervening. George straightened his tie with a trembling hand. Alan collapsed into an armchair and began to sob like a child. I understood perfectly why: in condemning George and our adventure he was also condemning all that had inspired his efforts during the last two years.

It is quite true there was reason enough to condemn George, but there was just as much reason to admire him. To my mind, what was important was not to know whether George was admirable or damnable, but to decide what attitude, whether of admiration or condemnation, we were going to adopt to give meaning to our lives.

*   *   *

We had come to the time when we had to choose, yet we realized that we were at the age when one has least ability for making a choice and least energy for putting into practice what one has chosen to do.

On one side there was the Marvellous Kingdom, far from noise and the world of men, yet at our very door, immense and perilous, a forest of Brocéliand, a cave of the Nibelungs, a temple of the Holy Grail, wonderful realm of silence and solitude, so well protected, so well isolated, so dangerously pure that it made us giddy.

On the other side was the land and people, what George called "the swarming of people parked on all that emerges from the sea", the comforting swarm of people among which God had had us born, among which old Rebufat had died.

Had we the right to anticipate and reject everyday life?

Had we the right to run useless risks and to make others run them, to juggle with our lives for no purpose?

In itself the loss of the statue did not mean much to me. In fact, in one way I was not sorry that we no longer had that as an excuse. Thus, we now had to judge our actions according to their true motives: useless adventure and wanton risks, risks the full extent of which we knew after that last accident to Claud.

After that the choice we made was made in the full realization of the way we were deciding to go.

*   *   *

I did not know what I wanted. I went to George.

219

"Are we going to go just the same?" I asked.

But George did not reply. His eyes avoided mine. In the corridor, he stopped beside our equipment that was standing there ready; furtively his hand caressed the heavy steel cylinders that were charged beyond the theoretical safety limit, at 400 lb.

Why, I kept asking myself, why had we thrust our way into the heart of the Marvellous Kingdom: for Professor Hornbostel's sea-slugs? for the statue? for the pride of dangers faced and difficulties overcome? or simply for the delight of what we saw? Or was it just that we confided our bodies to the sea and our souls to God?

*   *   *

"Get out the apparatus, we're going to dive."

We were back at our first cove, though whether for a farewell visit or to make a fresh start we did not know. George had made no pronouncement since Claud's accident and the scene with Alan. There was, of course, nothing to the diving we were going to do there; our equipment was ready, the depth slight.

In silence we put on the equipment once again. Our hands went to the chromium-plated wheels and a faint hissing made the valves seem alive. There was nothing to this, for we were just going below once more to drink of the philtre again, to yield our souls to the spell, to cull the forbidden fruits.

There was little sea and the swell made the grasses and algae sway in the rhythmical movements you see in animated cartoons. The frontier rock rose up straight ahead like a fantastic steeple, but it no longer meant anything to us. One leap sent us over the brink to dive headlong into the abyss trailing bubbles behind us. Our frogmen's feet raised a grey cloud. We flattened out and sped on towards more rocks.

Suddenly there was the miracle of the golden beach. Eighty feet down and the water was as clear as clear could be, and there it was, a little luminous beach, a private paradise. Blue shadows danced and played about it. George stretched out an arm in front and did a dream of a slow somersault, rolling himself in a glistening mantle of his own bubbles. The flat shadows dispersed. We had the beach to ourselves. At the foot of a nearby slab of rock some pale alcyonium spread its deformed fingers. What could they have in common with Aeolus' daughter and the fabulous birds that calm the sea? Mythological memories, Ovid and Virgil.

George rose to go back to the surface. His frogmen's feet went up and up and disappeared.

An enormous pinnate, covered with tiny concretions like a bee's nest, closed up at our approach. Sometimes, they say, you can find a pink pearl in them. From them, as from other shells, tridachnes or hammer-shell, comes the solid byssus.

Philip braced himself and tore it loose. The sand rose in dense swirls round him and the little beach was blotted out. We won't cut our names on the mother-of-pearl inside the shell. We won't make any mark.

George traced us back to the source of our stream of bubbles. With a clenched fist he stabbed the water: "That way. We're going back . . ."

*   *   *

Back on land and walking home along the corniche road we saw a "pirate", one of the few swimmers who break the law and hunt in diving equipment. He slipped into the water most discreetly, the big cylinder of a Le

Prieur at his chest, and a long Douglas with its mortal javelin already pointing towards the depths. We saw him disappear, but the breaking of his bubbles on the surface betrayed his position infallibly. George had his Cousteau on his back.

"A mask! Give me a mask," he roared in the tone of King Richard demanding a horse on Bosworth field.

"George, you're mad. Your apparatus is empty."

"Not at all. I still have the reserve."

He tore down the slope, kicked off his sandals, and slid into the sea in his shorts and shirt, without his frog feet. Not having a weighted belt he struggled for a second or two before he got away from the surface, and then we saw the two strings of bubbles, one continuous, the other intermittent, join and mingle.

Later George told us that he had got right above the "pirate" at about twenty feet and had at once torn the big mask off his face. The man had struggled in a veritable explosion of bubbles, and George had hauled him gasping to the rocks.

The man's gun was gone, no doubt reposing on the bottom of the hole fifty feet or more down, which was all to the good. While he spluttered and dribbled salt water, the gentle Alan dealt him violent blows in the pit of the stomach. (To make him vomit, so he told us afterwards, and added: "That's what you always do with people who are half-drowned.")

"I'll sue you!"

George was very calm:

"You've had your medicine. Lucky for you I bothered to fish you out. No, don't thank me. Your gun's gone, though. You know you mustn't dive with diving equipment when using a gun. You know its illegal, don't you? Well, that's all finished now."

When we were certain he was not going to die, we left him to his own devices. We never heard any more about it.

*   *   *

We were back at George's house, where in the hall, in its stand of wrought iron, now stood the amphora he had fished up the previous month near Marseilles. Antique and rough, he called it "Nausicaa's amphora", but the pious Alan insisted it should be the "Woman of Samaria's amphora".

There was a story attached to that amphora: George was trudging along the bottom with it towards the sling hanging from the boat, holding it with one hand by its rough terra cotta point and with the other inserted in its mouth which was encrusted and caked, when a large conger that had been sleeping inside uncoiled and put its head out. It remained there for some seconds, stuck in the narrow neck which was partially obstructed by George's hand, weaving its head from side to side like a dragon guarding a treasure. George, fascinated, stopped and stood still. This, however, was a benevolent dragon, and it resumed its outward progress, the cold sinuous body, oiled with mucus, slithering along George's hand and wrist till the whole conger was out. When it had vanished into the haze George, still clutching his amphora, staggered on across the uneven sea-bed.

*   *   *

We had just been diving and as we lay and rested, while our masks and apparatus lay soaking in fresh water, we relived and remembered that other world. We felt a friendly complicity for all that lived in dangerous liberty beneath the sea: the conger that had so kindly vacated its amphora for us, the nimble *sars*, the timid grey mullet, all the creatures that had lent us their beach that afternoon, even the whip-tailed sting ray, and the big moraena that but for us the "pirate" perhaps would have killed. All our anger with the man had evaporated. That belonged already to the past. We were left with just our problem.

*   *   *

Just before dinner that evening we received a visit from Scout Master Maurice, grave in the exercise of his function of lay director of conscience. As such he lectured us. It was all there: our Scout Promise, our duty to our neighbour, the egotistical pride of our going off by ourselves, of our setting ourselves apart, our "diving beyond reality", our duty to the community from which we had not the right to withdraw, our lives for which we would have to render account to God, which were given us for the good of others, and which we did not have the right to risk for trifles. Apparently neither the final loss of the statue, the financial check of our expedition, the accident to Claud, to say nothing of all the other accidents we had carefully hushed up but which would all eventually come to light, none of these seemed to have taught us our lesson since we had started all over again that afternoon: we had been diving again, tempting God again, again risking our time, our strength and our lives, those inestimable benefits for which we would one day have to account. Alan, Philip, Claud and I were poor ignoramuses, and not really responsible; George was the one responsible and he incorrigible.

The Scout Master's voice was thick and vehement. George and he faced each other. The one heavy and solid, hair cut short, filling the arm-chair, hands firmly on the arms, while George in his loose pullover and open neck hopped from one foot to the other, forelock dancing,

Right: As the swimmer goes underground bubbles rise; some will be caught and held among the crevices of the rocky roof

Below: When bubbles ceased to escape he was hoisted out and on to the jetty and his mask was quickly taken off. In about five minutes he was full of life again; then there was argument as to what had caused him to faint

Some recruits take to it quickly; others, even excellent swimmers, never manage it. Here a youngster under instruction goes down on a rope

hands nervously playing with a mother-of-pearl pocket knife, and in his eyes an expression of sorrow, confusion and occasional gleams of revolt.

"Well, what are you going to do?"

The Scout Master was forcing himself to speak in a neutral, almost indifferent tone of voice; but I could sense that he was anxious and eager. While, of course, he was genuinely concerned for our safety, I wondered whether his exhortations to prudence and his reminders of duty to one's neighbours might have had behind them some element of pique and the desire to put an end to an adventure that had dethroned him. If we gave way, it would be a striking revenge for him.

All that, however, did not really matter. We were not concerned with the motives of Scout Master Maurice; we were open to reason and it was quite possible for him to convince us by sound arguments that these were good grounds for changing.

In a flash I had a vision of what my life would be like if I yielded to the Scout Master's arguments, the things I should have to give up, all the little cowardly acts I should be daily forced to perform. Yet would that not be an act of detachment, a sacrifice of that vanity of vanities which courage is.

I remembered the lassitude I had felt on the island in the evening after our last dive and I wanted to laugh. It would be funny if I were to switch from deep-water diving to working at a boys' club. That seemed less silly than the Scout Master's herbarium and much more compelling. I felt a sudden urge to bow to him, to savour the joys of capitulation, and I wondered whether that constituted an act of grace or a temptation.

George shut his knife. It made a sharp little click. The Scout Master got up.

"I think he's right", Alan said, once we had heard the hall door close. George cried out at that:

"He's not. We're free. Free to choose, free to risk, as free in life, as we are in the sea."

* * *

I pressed George to revolt, to cut his moorings and go off despite everybody and everything. The others could not understand; they had no knowledge of the waving fields, the little golden beach, the seagreen light in which we stretched imponderable, the virgin jungle and the strange beings as in a magician's garden, the fascinating blue abyss in which our bubbles rose and swayed. They could not know. They had never felt the keen stab of pleasurable fear that we knew. They had never soared through the heart of our marvellous and perilous kingdom. They were chained to their *terra firma* where there were no surprises and all laws had been fixed and settled for centuries. They had the minds of prisoners; content or not, they were in prison.

The live creatures we brought up were an embodiment of this misunderstanding. Lovely sea-fans broke in the fresh air, swaying anemones turned into small sticky lumps, sea-slugs became viscous as soon as they left the water, spirographs retracted in fear and became brown sticks. In the sunlight of the world of man our dreams vanished between our fingers.

How could those who did not know understand that we were under the spell for ever and so were compelled thus "futilely" to risk our youth and play with our lives?

25

WE were in George's room with its galleon lamp-shade, books by Lawrence, Saint-Exupery and Larigaudie, and now on the mantelpiece a model made by poor old Rebufat. On the walls were the big naval charts which showed the position of wrecks and on which were recorded our more interesting dives.

This was our sanctuary, our holy of holies. George's hand caressed a chart. Slowly his finger moved down from north to south following the coast. The finger halted an instant between the sounding-lines where groups of letters indicated the nature of the bottom, then it moved on again. Little rings and in the centre of each a figure giving the depth to which mast and superstructure protruded from the bottom, each was the symbol of a wreck, a conventional sign for a ship gone down in relatively shallow water and still liable to become uncovered at low water, old hulks that the sea was demolishing bit by bit. And now among the buoys, the lights and the sea-marks, at the entrance to frequented channels, portentous tiny letters: Wreck, wreck.

Those marks and figures had a tale to tell us, made the charts take on colour and became alive. That mark there, half a mile or so off Cape Bear, that was *Saumur* to which we had dived the previous spring. She had been torpedoed during the Occupation and gone down with her cargo of iron-ore and Italian crew. Now crayfish had taken the Italians' place; they swarmed everywhere among the shattered plates.

And so other circles and other figures: *Alice Robert*,

banana boat, covered by 45 feet of water, at 145 feet, dredged to 75 feet. I can still see her, strewn with helmets and a litter of other equipment. *Saint-Lucien*, freighter, covered by 70 feet of water at 140 feet, dredged to 65 feet. A Spaniard. . . . Submarine *Astric*, lost in 130 feet: extent of wreck 58 feet, dredged to 55 feet. None has seen her since she went down during the First World War. With hatches closed she must be like a great shark, slowly and inexorably settling into the mud.

Then there was an unknown of 200 feet lying 107° off the Cape Bear light at 300 feet, but that was inaccessible. To man it was just a different note in the crackling of the echo-sounder, a peak in the recording band. Only the sound-waves could get down there and, rebounding from the iron, come back to tell those above that there was something too geometrical to be a rock, a man-made hull.

There was something compelling about those great depths and their forbidden fruit. George's hand described a gesture in the air, and fell back on to the chart again. His eyes clouded at the thought of those wrecks corroded and caked, rusty yet luxuriant, sordid and sumptuous, dead to man yet swarming with life; and then he spoke the word *Makassar*, and that made us think of *San Gennaro* lying at 650 feet and Captain Ferrero alone inside her, somewhere off Cape Figari.

And there were others and still others: wreck—wreck —wreck; and in the blanks on the chart innumerable other wrecks whose position was not known, all the steamers, barques, torpedo-boats, corvettes, galleys, submarines, ships of the line, tramps and the indefinable, a comradely jumble of centuries and flags, all as solemn and silent as the *Flying Dutchman*.

Scout Master Maurice and those like him would never glide down like disembodied spirits to inspect units of

that great fleet of ghosts. They would never force the door
of a chart-room at 130 feet, where perhaps some gold-
striped officer like Alan's father had slowly disintegrated.
Their fingers, white with cold, would never clutch the
spokes of some old wheel. They would never know our
Marvellous Kingdom with its treasures, dragons, magic
flowers, Ali-Baba's caves, and squadrons of lost ships.
They would always cling to their world, which was the
world of the living, and keep to the sun and the air.

Besides they would look at the sea through some magic
device that would make their wonderment fall short of
ours. To them everything would be less beautiful, the
coral less red in the beam of their torches, the sea-fans
smaller, the wrecks less enchanting. That would be so,
because all those things would be given them, they would
not have conquered them. While we, before knowing the
coral, the sea-fans, the wrecks or the blue at 160 feet,
had had to draw plans and manufacture weird apparatus;
and when our plans were bad, we suffocated in our
apparatus, and the salt water found its way into our
mouths; we had to keep starting all over again.

All the hours and the effort we had put into it, all the
agony of diving naked in winter, the extent of our fears
and the risks of death we ran, all had gradually traced the
features of our adventure. And all those risks and efforts
and suffering made the coral more red, the sea-fans larger,
the wrecks more sumptuous, and the blue of the water
deeper.

Ought we to be sorry for Scout Master Maurice and
those like him, or envy them for being saved the anguish
and the pleasure.

I remember when I was small I had a big book of tales
and legends of the sea. I was quite bowled over by the
text and pictures: drakkars with red sails made from the

nails of the dead, enchanted gardens on isles of the blessed, gentlemen of fortune with scalloped collars, the grim fires of Cornish wreckers, dramas of the sun, fog and water, of mingled sea and sky, and the occasional phantom figure of some ghostly vessel.

In our big, silent library I would wait till nightfall, fearful and yet desirous. Nothing obliged me to open the book and, though I hesitated sometimes for a long time, in the end I always did so and read.

* * *

George thrust his head into his hands and groaned. No doubt he regretted the days when all our obstacles were external ones, the days of technical difficulties and of doing things in secret. Now that we were free, with no material impediments, we were left to face our responsibilities and were less free than ever.

George got up, walked across to the window and looked out.

"My uncle, who is a historian, told me that in the Middle Ages, after the capture of Acre by the Saracens, and the collapse of the Frankish Kingdom of Jerusalem, some knights of the Order of Templars, rather than go back to Europe and their castle-barracks, intrigues and temptations, decided to head southwards, dressed in Arab garb, away from their former companions. That is why, apparently, certain Arab peoples still have emblazoned shields and straight swords with cruciform guards."

"They were unfaithful to their Order", said Alan softly.

"But faithful to adventure, to the sand-dunes, to battle, to the purity of the desert. Whatever you do, you are always true to one thing and a traitor to another, pure in this, impure in that. They were, no doubt, venturesome knights, the most venturesome perhaps.

*   *   *

George had decided that we must take a decision as a whole, and we had assembled in his room as at the time of our first council five years before. As the senior it was up to me to speak first.

"George, I will abide by whatever you decide," I said.

"I too", Philip said.

"And I", said Claud and Alan together.

George sighed, both proud and wearied at the thought of again having to shoulder a responsibility that he had wished to divide among us all.

"To-morrow", he said.

We got up to go, but George held me back.

"You, Francis. Stay a bit, will you?"

The others left. I felt older and stronger, able to take my share of the burden, not because of an arithmetical division of responsibilities, but because of the personal appeal.

We were weighing the Scout Master's argument that ours was an ineffectual adventure without utility. Our counter-argument was that it was perhaps gratuitous, but that we thereby increased our stature. There was little doubt what the Scout Master's answer to that would be:

"There you are! Egoism. Exalting your own persons!"

Those were just words which we could counter with other words:

"It is not us we exalt, but Man through us."

And the scornful reply would be:

"Pagan humanism."

But we would retort:

"Not pagan humanism at all. Is not the best way to honour God who created man to exalt the divine part of man?"

We felt strong enough to deal with the Scout Master in the game of splitting hairs, but did it get us any further? We were still hesitant.

It was already late when the bell rang. As on that evening of St. George's Day it was Alan. There was a certain constraint between him and George since that scene after Claud's accident, and they shook hands awkwardly.

"I've been thinking it over", said Alan, and sat down on the divan.

Outwardly it was still the same Alan of St. George's Eve, the Alan who had blubbed at night in the tent, who had panicked when he dived, who had saved me at the desert island and who obediently swallowed what medicine his mother wanted. His gaze seemed to brush us even more slightly than usual, to be turned inwards.

Carefully I scrutinized this agglomeration of cells that bore the name Alan and wondered what made it appeal to me more than any other agglomeration of human cells. As he spoke Alan's face wore his usual grave, almost tragic expression. He did not mention the Scout Master, but spoke of the sea, the cold, the sharp rocks, the nocturnal dives and the tortuous watery tunnels of the subterranean rivers.

I watched his face as he talked. Behind it lay a whole world of ideas, of desires, efforts, memories, a living treasure that animated it with imperceptible little quivers. Behind it were the sea with its waves, coral caves and wrecks, and my own life that he had saved.

Surely Alan was not just a simple agglomeration of living cells, but a reality gradually fashioned by his own acts freely performed, a reality that was far above the utilitarian calculations of our Scout Master, that defied all arithmetic since it partook of man and thereby of God. All that would enrich Alan, would enrich man and thereby would enrich other men as well and would glorify God. It was like a composer who in correcting his manuscript enriches some chord and thereby enhances the piece, in that all the other chords acquire greater value by his having done that. And the composer is glorified.

From that moment I knew that our adventure was an ideal. It did not consist of the coral, nor of the sea-fans, nor of the fish, nor of the golden statue, nor even of the interest of well-designed equipment, for otherwise the Scout Master would have been right; but our adventure was the sea itself, the risk, the whip of the waves, the anguish and the effort, all things that, freely accepted, helped to mould Alan, enhanced him, and thereby enhanced mankind and honoured God.

Of course it would be stupid to risk one's life for coral and even for a golden statue, if the coral and the golden statue did not thereby become extra precious for having been considered worth a man's confronting the sea and risking his life to obtain them.

Adventure is never that towards which we are marching, but that against which we are struggling in a struggle that compels us to build ourselves up alone and not to refuse God. And that towards which we were aiming originally is subsequently given us in greater measure—or refused, as were Brother Antoine's cave and the golden statue.

But that no longer mattered.

From that moment, too, I had the certitude that Christianity was the one and only refuge for adventurers like us, for whom the only justification of their goal is that they have to strive to attain it.

Those whose ideal takes the form of building a human city of a certain form, require to see the city complete with stout ramparts, covered markets, and well-ventilated schools. And no more. If the city could be built all at once at the wave of a wand, it would be no less beautiful for that; but on the other hand he would be a traitor and worthy of the gallows, who delighted only in the act of building and lingered as he put the stones together; in fact he would be both traitor and madman, for there is no point to the stones till the building is finished.

But Christianity does not wish to build a city however beautiful; it wants to build a Christian, that is to say Man. And Man can only build himself up by marching and conquering. For him conquest is already possession, the march an encounter, and His God could well say to him: "Thou shalt not look for Me, if thou has not already found Me."

Until that moment we had been running away; we had despised people and had revolted against our human destiny. But Alan had been sent to us, and now for the first time our setting out would not be an escape away from Man, but conquest in the name of Man, no longer revolt, but acceptance. One thing alone was necessary: to live one's life, that is, live the life God had dreamed for one as a father imagines in his mind a future for his child.

Until then we had been brothers, as voluntary exiles are brothers, equally poor in being tied to nothing. Henceforward we would be brothers as are the soldiers of the advance guard, equally rich in the army that follows after.

As we had done five years earlier, we went to the chaplain to ask his blessing. He gave it us and recommended prudence.

The next day was Sunday, and in the afternoon I went

to the Church Hall where I knew I should find the Scout Master, to tell him our decision. I had got George to see that there was no point in his coming.

There the Scout Master was with some new recruits. They had formed a ring round a circle drawn on the ground, and into this they were trying to pull or thrust each other with a great deal of scuffling and heels being dug in. From high above came a hum and, looking up, I saw three tiny specks slowly moving through the air tracing a triple trail of vapour. They were so high that it took them more than a minute to pass the red brick chimney and get in among the branches of the plane tree. I could imagine the pilots in their masks and protective suits, breathing pure oxygen and correcting the position of their planes with a slight pressure of their palms: were they not like divers on an aquaplane?

The bell began to ring for evening service; a whistle sounded and the Scouts fell in.

"Pull up your stockings. Get your scarves straight."

Nothing missed the Scout Master's eye.

In the sky overhead the glistening vapour plume was slowly beginning to dissolve.

I decided to wait till after the Service before speaking to our Scout Master, so I followed the others into the coolness of the church. A queer feeling came over me as I knelt there at the back. Again I was aware of a strange temptation. The Scout Master's little ruses made me want to laugh and yet they had an inexplicable power over me. Again I suddenly felt that I wanted to give everything up, to join their silly game in the courtyard so as to feel my hands clasping other hands, to have something other than risk. I felt that I did not want to think any more about the three pilots high in the sky or of our fugitive flights beneath the sea; I wanted to give it all up, to stick to the earth henceforward, to the world of man, to be one of the crowd.

That would give total security in perfect humility; but that too would be to serve, because it takes plenty of humble works, plenty of anonymous devotion, to send one single representative of Man 35,000 feet into the air or 230 feet beneath the sea. I supposed I too should be told to pull up my stockings and see that my scarf was straight, and I would obey the Scout Master as I obeyed George when he sent me willy-nilly down to the wreck.

But no. It was not possible. Philip, Claud, George and Alan were waiting for me. My post was among them and not at the side of the Scout Master. And, besides, why change direction now? Was not the joy the same for all, the joy that you had when you did not search but just stuck to your post, honourably?

When we came out from the church the vapour trail had gone. The pilots were probably back on the ground, men once more, filled with the joy of a job well done, very much like the Scout Master after a successful game.

I found Maurice and told him of our decision. He shrugged his shoulders and turned away. I had wanted to say that we had been wrong in condemning him, but that he too was wrong to go on condemning us; but the words would not come.

As I left, I had a glimpse of a lawn where a fat nun was in charge of some shrill-voiced children; there too was the sacristan trotting back from attending to his candles, and nearby the Scout Master was organizing a game of basket ball. We were all in the same boat, surely, a boat almost as old as the world and sailing for God knows where. Our posts were different, that was all. Why try to oppose what is just different?

I remembered George in the boat coming back from

our last trip to the island, sitting scanning the shore through his glasses and raving at the swarms of humanity on the earth to which we were being forced to return. That day, George had understood nothing. It was not a question of the Marvellous Kingdom being distinct from the earth of Man, a thing apart; but the Marvellous Kingdom was a prolongation of the earth of Man, a place to be conquered in the name of Man.

As I walked back through the port I felt myself the possessor of a great secret. And I felt ties with the entire crew.

26

A BREEZE was swelling the sail and we were off. As
we drew abreast of the last buoy it rose up on a wave
to see us pass and its green eye lit up with envy. Later, in
the evening, as we were about to enter upon our first night
we lit stars in the water with our navigation lights. We
were the messengers of earth on the sea.

Let the Scout Master write his reports about our
insubordination and our morbid taste for danger. What
did we care! The wind was blowing and the sea thunder-
ing on the rocks. Of course he was right when he said
that it is fine to construct and to build. In speaking of his
precious soul Man often uses the terms of the architect:
town, house, temple, citadel. Yet it is also a fine thing to
venture, like a ship off the slip and at last lifting to the
swell. What use would the workmen be if the swell were
never allowed to lift a ship? A ship at sea is lovelier than
a fortress anchored for ever to the earth, for it has both
balance and movement, adventure and direction; in it
is the will of man and it faces the hazard of God's
intentions.

A ship at sea is the loveliest thing in the world. I would
like to lead my life in open waters, like a ship.

But I remember what we had promised the Chaplain.
Though our own masters we had not the right to hazard
the ship God had entrusted to us. So we were going to be
sensible and not juggle with our lives any more. But each
time that should become necessary, we would set that life
of ours on the scales of the balance.

"O God, in exchange for this risk freely accepted,

grant me that which I desire." There are so many things that are worth as much and more than life.

For the second time our path has lain round the submarine pedestal of our desert island. To-morrow it will be two months since we returned to these abrupt slopes carpeted with algae and sponges, the cave of the blue lobster, the spirographs' gully, the plain of the sea-fans and the wreck of *Makassar* now with a gaping hole cut with a blow-pipe at the level of No. 3 hold. On the island itself nothing had changed; the little spring was still sobbing and we only had to put fresh white sea-fans on the grave of the sailor, the winter weather having rotted and dispersed the others.

We had taken nothing from the sea. In three days, when we returned to Man's earth, we would take back just a few photographs, some corals and, scribbled on the blank pages of my diving diary, these notes about the past, whether remote or still recent.

Now I have come to the end of my notes, the end of the tale of our adventure. Now, the record of happenings must give place to a record of hopes and intentions: "We have done" must become "We will do—if God pleases."

What does the future hold? I cannot say. Next summer, perhaps, we shall be running our fingers over the columns of the Grecian town submerged off Cape Artemision. Perhaps we shall be seeing in the view-finder of our camera the streamlined shadows of the sharks among which Larigaudie bathed off Rurutu . . . unless George and Claud continue with the Swede Zetterstrom's experiments and succeed in achieving the mixed hydrogen-oxygen respirator that ought to do away with all possibility of narcosis and so let us achieve the extraordinary depth of 480 feet.

Perhaps . . .

In two days we shall again be embarking all our equipment: in *Sagitta*; rubber suits, cylinders, compressor, rubber dinghy, Cot reanimating apparatus, etc., and we shall leave this island whose foundations underwater we know far better than what lies above the surface. When we are gone, the rocks lying bathed in the pale autumnal sunshine will know only the wheeling of the crying petrels. But under the sea in the prodigious exuberance of life there, our absence will make no difference. All will repeat itself immutably, from the beginning right to the end, happily preserved from evolution and the intervention of Man.

Cold and bad weather were driving us away. For our last few dives we had had to put on our waterproof suits of foam rubber that moulded itself to our bodies. They were not so much garments as a sort of second skin, thick and insensitive, because of which our flesh was not so aware of the rigorous cold of the livid sea, and which gave us the freedom of nakedness that had little or no thermal response. On emerging from the water, one of the others would grip you under the arms and a third pulling in the opposite direction would peel off the suit, like skinning a rabbit, and leave you astonished to find yourself shivering and defenceless against the icy wind.

* * *

"Look, a shoal of sardines being chased by pelamides, I expect."

Off the point flashes seemed to be coming from the sea, describing graceful arcs and raining back into the green water.

"The pelamides must be behind."

It was the first time I had heard the word and it made me think of a cruel dynasty of ancient Grecian kings.

"Come on, we'll try and intercept."

We galloped out to the point and flung ourselves in with our masks. George set the pace and I was beginning to feel I should have to give up when a bluish torpedo with a chromium-coloured belly emerged out of the haze; then another and another, cruel, thoroughbred carnivorous brutes, the terror of the small fry. Disdainfully they slewed to starboard, dipped and shot downwards.

We only had masks with breathing tubes and had to stay where we were, stuck to the surface. When they had gone, two or three other silvery flashes gleamed in the depths beneath. Perhaps, thanks to us, the sardines were able to escape.

Regretfully we swam back to shore. A quarter of a mile away, speeding south, we saw the round see-sawing back of a dolphin surmounted by its black fin. There must have been a bit of wind farther out, for through the glasses the line of the horizon appeared broken and jagged, with a thousand white unevennesses.

It was the 6th October and we were racing the weather. We had poured the last of our petrol into the tank of the compressor, for George wanted to dive again, to have a few more minutes under the sea. All night he and Claud had worked by the light of our acetylene lamp replacing the masks of the three-cylinder equipment with ordinary mouthpieces with duck-beak valves and underwater hunter's masks. They had dispensed with the warning whistles, gauges and reversing switches, so that we were able to start on two cylinders at once, keeping only one in reserve. By about ten o'clock, *Sagitta* was rolling gently in the swell. The little ladder fixed to her starboard side made it easy to get into the water. In we went, one by one, all, that is, except Alan who was to take *Sagitta* back to the island, flippered feet groping to find the last step.

Involuntarily our breathing quickened as we went under, then our hands opened, let go of the uprights and we were in a different world. With mouthpieces firmly in place and cylinders properly strapped to our backs, we felt ready for congers or anything.

Fifty feet brought us to the undulating valley planted with little pockets of algae. Philip levelled out, thrust his arm into the rocky jaws of a crevice, rummaged for an instant or two then withdrew his gauntletted hand clutching the plates of a crayfish. We tried our luck in turn; George lost his catch and saw it vanish into the blue, but Claud was more fortunate and was able to brandish his prey. I soon found a shell to grasp and drew it out without difficulty, only to discover that it was empty, just a shell that had been cast.

Suddenly, there was no more air, the bottles were exhausted. Groping, my fingers found the chromium-plated wheel and turned it. There was an answering hiss as the 330 lb. in the third cylinders divided itself equally among the three: 110 lb. in each. Then I closed the tap again and resumed breathing on just the two cylinders. The 110 lb. in the third would be a reserve, capable of being split again to give nearly 40 lb. in each, 40 lb. with which to get back to the surface.

Now the two cylinders were empty again, but the last 40 lb. got me to the surface. Heavens, how far away the shore was! I spat out the mouthpiece and replaced it with the ordinary breathing tube I had put in my belt. Keeping the cylinders submerged so as not to tire ourselves with their weight, the three of us swam along parallel like a shoal of porpoises, just scratching the surface. If I turned my head a little, I could see Claud on my left and Philip on my right. From time to time George raised his masked head and checked our direction. Claud smiled at me. His face was twisted by the pull of his mask, so that his brows were oddly raised, giving him an air of perpetual astonishment. Triumphantly he brandished his crayfish.

There was the shore with black rocks white and smoking with breakers. In a final farewell George made an ordinary swimmer's dive to the bottom and back again. Without our steel cylinders we were debarred from long stays under water; reduced to our own resources we were neither shark nor conger, frail creatures that at the best could be called sub-aquatic.

*　　　*　　　*

I have just been having a long discussion with George on nitrogen narcosis, that inevitable phenomenon that makes all diving below 130 feet so dangerous. Under high pressure the heavy nitrogen ends by becoming fixed in the tissues of the body and thereby causes euphoria, a curious, pathetic state in which you feel no desire to rise to the surface; and this is followed by black-out.

If we had managed to reach greater depths, it was only because the infiltration of the nitrogen is initially slow and progressive. The narcosis does not begin to take effect until you are down at 130 feet, but even then it is possible to trick it, to dive much deeper into the heart of the forbidden zone and to escape again at once, before the intoxication has had time to take effect, before the supreme indifference comes, before death arrives.

In order to keep track of the effects of the narcosis George quite seriously suggested the following procedure: at regular intervals to try multiplying a two-cipher number by 7, 8 or 9. When the mind is no longer able to do the multiplication, you must surface. The rigorous application of this procedure would make diving out of the question for me, for I am incapable of managing it even on the surface.

Because of this narcosis before you could dive really deep the nitrogen in the air would have to be replaced by some lighter gas, such as helium or hydrogen, to the extent of 96 per cent. from 130 feet onwards.

It was an intriguing problem. It is not simply a question of gaining a few strokes downwards, but if Man could dive to 600 or 900 feet he would have possession of the vast continental plateau, instead of just the narrow fringe of the littoral.

But then the cachalots which breathe God's good air, they dive to 600 and 900 feet and come up again. How do they manage? We know that they go so deep from finding in their digestive systems fish that only live at those depths. According to Claud, the explanation is that the cachalot does not store up air to breathe before diving, but rather a reserve of blood that is already oxygenated. Thus all the respiratory economy is performed on the surface beforehand, so that there is no risk of what George calls a "deplorable phenomenon".

*   *   *

7 October. The gulls have been crying all night. Each time one passed over the tent its cry rose, then died away behind the moaning of the wind in a long wail like that of a soul in torment. I know now whence comes the superstition that gulls are the reincarnated spirits of drowned sailors. We slept little and badly. At dawn, as we emerged one by one, the big birds fled, but only to re-form in a garland wheeling and screaming round the rock that tops the south east of the island. A swell was breaking on the steep shore. As each wave retreated it left all the hollows

in the rock streaming with a thousand murmuring cascades.

Like the poor passengers of *Liban* smashed on the island of Maire, those drowned when *Makassar* went down ten years before must have been wedged against that flange of rock, before they slowly sank to the lairs of the lobster and cray-fish.

The weather was bad and there could be no question of diving. All morning we struggled to charge our cylinders for one last effort. The two-stroke motor that worked the compressor refused to start. At last, about noon, it consented to work and its stutter sent the birds flying out to sea again. Then the compressor broke down. The gauge for the high-pressure stage obstinately refused to go beyond 120, while the medium-pressure gauge went up to giddy heights. Although we had cleaned it frequently, there was probably some dirt that was hampering the working of the valves.

Whatever it was, we did not feel very reassured. George alone whistled cheerfully, hands deep in the pockets of his greasy shorts. Then suddenly the valve freed and everything became normal again. George has promised that for our last dive to-morrow he will take me below 195 feet.

* * *

I have taken advantage of this afternoon's forced inactivity and re-read the first fifty pages of this diary of our dives. How strangely it reads now. It is so full of paganism and stupid self-conceit that I wonder I could have written it. Of course, I must have changed considerably during this last year, since our second camp on the island, rather like that friend of mine, now a navigator with Air-France, who told me on one of the last occasions we met that, when he was going to catechism class, he used to draw aeroplanes on the margin of his prayer book, but now, when he is flying at night and plotting his position by the stars, he thinks of God.

It is the same with all of us, we used to flatten our young noses against the glass of the ship-chandlers' windows, now we walk past without seeing them. On the threshold of an adventure all one's powers are tensed waiting for the first conquests to be attempted, then one starts making discoveries and mind and heart begin to marvel and a whole mythology blossoms out. But always there comes a time when you leave the myths and dream of the sole God.

And the adventure of this latter stage is no longer the domain toward which one is making, it is not even the dangerous, secret garden where you part the branches in order to surprise the divinities; the adventure is within you, has become a state of soul, permanently there to deal with the calls made on it, no matter whence they come.

Thus the adventure is never to refuse, always to be willing.

It seems to me, however, that you cannot omit any stage in this progression; and that is why I distrust those who, from adolescence or profess to despise courage, or to prefer it to other virtues. No doubt Plato was right to make courage the last of the virtues, but you still have to be courageous in order to assess courage at its true, though slight value. That, too, is why I distrust those who after adolescence devoutly turn to "boring and easy" good works. How can one really know if they have *chosen* these works, or whether they make do with them because they cannot fulfil themselves on other levels? How can one know that their humility is not weakness, their self-denial not lack of ability?

246

Instead of which the Venturer will know what he is giving. Being courageous, he will disdain courage; being efficient he will contemn action; rich, he will despise wealth.

*   *   *

Just before we left for the island this year someone who shall be nameless asked me:

"Francis, do you intend to marry later on?"

"Of course. I would like to have children."

"But adventure is for the solitary. If you do marry, you will have to give up your adventure and devote yourself to your love and your home."

"No, I won't", I replied.

That evening when I thought it over, I tried to put into words what it was had impelled me to say "no".

Fall back on the object of your love? You solely for me, and I solely for you? Must both shrink in stature? It has taken centuries of literature to find the beauty in these perfect marriages which are the kind Suzy the octopus celebrates, to glorify this reciprocal egoism, to establish the prestige of total giving. But love is not that: it is conquest, it is an unfolding.

I imagine that when a person has accepted to hazard his life and knows that he may be compelled to abandon everything without even time to give one backward look, he will find in the hours of love that his possession of the object of his love is more ardent for being more fragile, and that in talking with the object of his love he will find words that another would not have found, and in speaking to God of the object of his love prayers that another would not have composed.

And I believe that in the hour of battle he who loves and knows himself loved, who has had to tear himself away with feigned brutality in order to go, when he measures strength with death, he will feel himself at once stronger and greater because for his ideal he is risking the destiny of two.

*   *   *

I have found myself wondering about friendship. Whom did I like best: Philip, Claud, George or Alan. A bad question that, for it was impossible to answer, since friendship is above all an exchange, a sharing, and as there are few people with whom I do not feel able to share something, in one sense most are my friends. But of course such friendships would not be the same, since the exchanges would be made at different levels.

With this person I share the taste for a book—for one particular book and not another; with that I share a delight in the stars and the savour of their names. With yet another I may only share a night on the binge.

But with Philip, Claud, George, Alan it is the sharing of our adventures:

with Claud I share its technique
with Philip its exciting brutality
with George the joy of it
with Alan its fervour.

*   *   *

Down on the bottom by that headland with the palms George's body was swaying vertically like a piece of sea-weed. No, it was not George; perhaps it was Alan, or Philip. The mouthpiece had slipped from his teeth and was hanging on his chest like an amulet at the end of the long ringed tube that rested on his shoulders. His head had tilted back, the mouth was half-open, and from it a last bubble rose and sped upwards like a dove.

I must swim and get to him. Impossible. It was all hazy. The water was cold. I struggled desperately. Painfully I woke. Idiot! Dreams mean nothing. All the same, which of the four was it? Their regular breathing was scarcely audible in the silence of the night. I pulled up the blankets that had slipped off, glanced at the luminous dial of the watch hanging on the tent pole: three o'clock. Another four hours to sleep.

This morning, as planned, George and I put on our artificial skins and went down to take a last farewell of the plateau of the sea-fans, the spirographs' gully and haunt of the long-armed, and of the wreck. As the others equipped us, I had a feeling that this last dive would be in some way different from the others. George, in foam-rubber helmet like the headpiece of a coat of mail, looked unusually grave, and as Philip and Claud knelt to put on our frogmen's feet, I could not help thinking of the knights of old and their golden spurs.

Beyond the gully of the spirographs was an immense plain, its slope gentle enough to begin with, but then shelving more and more steeply. Wind and bad weather did not matter; under the sea it is always fine. George sped along by the bottom heading for the open and the deep. Above us followed the boat, ready to fish us out when we surfaced, and I could imagine Alan's face creasing with anxiety each time the patch of foam, in changing position, vanished between two waves.

We were over the wreck. I motioned towards the dark shape of the reef close on our right, but George just shook his head. He sped down faster and faster, diving into the haze. Every now and again he consulted the bathometer on his left wrist and then his watertight watch, then motioned to me: Come!

A flat shape moved ahead of us in heavy, flapping

progress, mouth in profile joined to large waving wings, slender pointed fuselage to which was fixed a horrible dart; a whip-tailed sting-ray. How fast it went! Corrugations passed along the trailing edge of its big fleshy wings, but whether they were muscular or merely caused by the passage of the water, I could not tell. A little farther on the ray pulled itself upright, rolled up and dropped to sprawl flat among the sea-fans.

I wanted to stop. Why go farther and farther down? I think I was afraid. We had taken only three minutes to reach the level of the wreck at 130 feet and must have been approaching 190 feet, if we were not already beyond it. I did not remember the figures exactly, but I seemed to remember that according to the table a dive of ten to fifteen minutes at that depth requires a halt of something like half an hour at ten feet before surfacing.

George went on and on. Should I follow him? How could I not?

Nitrogen narcosis! Stop, George, stop. That's a barrier you cannot force, one you cannot know is there, but which kills. Stop, George!

George stopped the movement of his feet, and put his wrist with the bathometer near my mask so that I could see the graduated scale: 225 feet. We had never been so deep. Around us were black fish, phantoms whose names I no longer knew.

Now I felt magnificently calm and courageous, and wondered why we had stopped, why we did not continue right to the heart of our Marvellous Kingdom. There we would savour our hour of truth. Let the dragons come! Ours was the treasure of the Nibelung; ours the goddess of wisdom. She had never been enclosed within the steel plates of the wreck, but was everywhere, spread throughout this luminous haze into which we were slowly penetrating like two souls. Or lower still, into the blue vault of the night pierced by pale phosphorescence. Why go back to the surface? Where was it anyway? Was it really in the direction of those bubbles that now seemed to be flowing ahead of me level with the immense, gently shelving plain? Where was the surface? Things had no weight, everything was topsy-turvy; there was no other indication but the mad bubbles that persisted in rolling zig-zag down the slope, instead of going back to the surface.

I would have stayed on there beside George in that great silence a long time, perhaps for ever, but George seized my wrist, shook me as though to wake me; then taking me under the arms he raised me out from the motionless bushes. For some time—how long I do not know—we glided on, one pressed to the other, in swift pursuit of our bubbles, leaving behind us those sea-fans which were the largest I had ever seen.

Suddenly the world seemed to tilt, the sea-floor reverted to the vertical and was cliff again. I realized that we had been rising at full speed all that time. At 130 feet I too began to move my feet, and so George and I ascended, face to face, without effort or fear, each of us the other's only reality in a universe that was inexorably blue.

In the boat as we went back to the island George looked at me with unseeing eyes, and I remembered the George of the cove and all the other Georges: at sea, in the heart of the Marvellous Kingdom, of the great helmet, of the kamikaze, of the free-dive equipment, of 35 feet, of 135 feet, of 225 feet. That day George and I had crossed the threshold of the temple.

Alan was the one of us to whom God had granted the gift of inner certitude, but for a few hours I too was to have it, for George and I were elevated to his level. The wind howled and the sea pounded on the rocks, yet as George and I walked side by side in that desolation of stone our hearts remembered the sumptuous cathedrals of silence and peace. For a few hours we were sure our souls were immortal. Soon the bustle of the world would be troubling our peace again and would destroy that glorious certitude, reduce it to a mere logical certitude. From certitude to conviction, from conviction to hypothesis. . . . Soon we would once more be wondering whether we had souls and suffering from a longing for God. For the moment, however, we were in possession of the Absolute. We heard neither the wind nor the sea, nor the shrill cries of the petrels. We heard only God and our souls. All that counted was that instant, that foretaste of eternity.

Was it not worth risking one's life for that?

EPILOGUE

Now that you have turned the last page of this story and are perhaps dreaming dreams and making plans, do not forget that the sea is always the sea and death is always death. Remember that, both for the sake of those for whom you may have the responsibility and for yourself.

This book was finished before the day when we waited in vain for one of us to surface. It had only needed the sea to get up suddenly, for him to be a few seconds late in making a manoeuvre so that he lost contact in the suddenly troubled waters, and for that to happen at the end of a patrol when, our cylinders being almost empty, our liberty of action was restricted.

We dived again, feeling that each second might be fatal; then the chief looked at his watch, drew his hand across his eyes and said:

"It's all over now. He *cannot* have any air left."

The column of bubbles had dried up for ever.

We continued to search beneath the screen of the breakers, through the live haze of particles in suspension, stirred up by the waves. We gave up the search when our bottles were empty, and then it was evening.

To my mind the price was heavy, and realizing that if you decide you would like to make the acquaintance of the Marvellous Kingdom there is a risk that you too one day may sink slowly towards the bottom, mask torn off, lungs filled with water and arms crossed, I almost regret having written this book.

Afterwards, there still being a little time before supper, the chief ordered one of us to take a light mask and go to the cave to check that our camera with automatic pressure was working properly, and that made me realize that everything was to continue, that we were to remain faithful to the one who had not come up, and that it was right that we should.

Indeed, is that not worth one's risking one's life for?

On one side are the few photographs, the few yards of film; on the other the money, the time, the effort and, above all, the corpses of the young men that always stake out the paths of disinterested enterprises.

It is Man's honour and greatness to try such experiments despite the apparent want of balance. The day when, on the eve of some undertaking, we begin to ask: will it pay? what use is it? on that day not even our social sense, our communal spirit, our rational economic organization, can make our civilization anything better than an association of resourceful animals: beavers, ants and termites. We shall no longer be men. We shall have betrayed ourselves.

The day after one of us had died diving, a group of loungers on the jetty of the little port expressed surprise that we had not even stopped going down. They could not understand that, and it disturbed them that they could not. I was there among them, a mackintosh covering my uniform, and I heard an old fisherman say:

"What do you expect? It's their idea."

The group then dispersed, though the reply was more of a puzzle than an explication. But in a way our companion had risked his life and died for his idea.

And, indeed, is that not worth risking your life for?

Yes, of course, even to-day, and above all yesterday. I am sure of that, and I would like to make you share my contrition. All conquest demands that you take risks, provided that you always see that you have the maximum of chances on your side, that you measure, meticulously, the share of danger to be left to the waves, the haze and the weight of the water.

The adventure lies not in death but in the struggle, and even death can have no point unless you have done everything to conquer it.

I decided not to include in this book certain things that I felt were too brutal, certain descriptions that were too horrible. First of all, out of consideration for you, but also because there are many true adventures that can suitably be placed in a fictionized account and others that it would be sacrilege to include, because they belong to the dead, not to the dead figures of fiction, but the real dead whom we have taken from the sea after hours of searching for them, livid and covered with sand, and whom we have had to strip painfully of their rubber suits and equipment.

It is a queer feeling, you know, to place between your teeth a mouthpiece that you know was clenched between the gums of one who died three days before.

It is to avoid that happening to you that I utter this warning:

After the first few successful dives you will feel yourself capable of everything in an easy, friendly universe. But beware. It is just when everything seems to be for the best that the accident can happen. Never forget that you are in a world if not hostile, then at least supremely indifferent, a world that can asphyxiate you in a few seconds without even an eddy reaching the surface.

I say that not to discourage you, but to prepare you; not to put you off, but to make you forearmed, not to lessen your desire, but to increase it.

Before you pull on the mask and strap to your back the heavy apparatus that will open for you the gates to our

Marvellous Kingdom, let me wish you, in the words of the old formula, "the courage of a lion" but also "the prudence of the serpent".

And—happy diving!